ENVIRONMENT 24/7

Building a Culture of Environmental Awareness

Gregory M. Anderson,
Richard C. Haut, Ph.D. & Tom Williams

ENVIRONMENT 24/7

Building a Culture of Environmental Awareness

Printed on 100% recycled & 100% post-consumer waste paper.

Greg Anderson
PO Box 131120
Spring, TX 77393
281.651.5648

Printed in the United States of America
ISBN: 978-0-9896605-0-1

Credits

Copy editing and proofreading	Positively Proofed, Plano, TX	info@PositivelyProofed.com
Design, art direction and production	Back Porch Creative, Plano, TX	info@BackPorchCreative.com

Contents

Introduction

When you go home today, will there be clean water to drink? Will climate change cause a natural disaster to strike your home? Will some type of spill alter our landscape for years to come?

Do you think these scenarios will only happen somewhere else?

Think again.

More than 11 percent of the world's population cannot access clean water at all, while the average person in The Woodlands, Texas, is using more than 68,000 gallons of water per year.

The National Academy of Sciences reports an average of 27 oil spills occur every day somewhere in the world, and the Valdez spill doesn't even make the list of the top 30 all-time largest. In 2012, there were 905 natural catastrophes worldwide, 93 percent of these being weather-related disasters. This figure was nearly 100 more than the 10-year annual average for these type of events.

Disturbing statistics? They disturbed us enough to write *Environment 24/7* to show how you, your family, co-workers and your company can dramatically improve the future health of Planet Earth … before it's too late to make a difference in our world.

Gregory Anderson and Robert Lorber's book, *Safety 24/7*, shows how a company's safety culture can positively change, and was the genesis for how to improve a company's environmental culture.

Nobody wants an environmental incident to occur. Companies try to eliminate incidents by making the environment a priority or writing additional policies and procedures … but incidents continue to happen. Why? Because they have left the human element out of the equation.

Environment 24/7 is a book about 'Building a Culture of Environmental Awareness,' positively transforming personal habits and company culture to create a cleaner, more environmentally healthy planet.

Just as *Safety 24/7* has helped save lives, it is our hope that *Environment 24/7* helps to save our ecosystems by illustrating that real change can only take place where there is an open mind and a willing heart.

1 The Alarm Sounds. The Challenge Begins.

Fred Jacobson guided his SUV onto the highway, trying not to become upset when, only a few minutes later, he found himself stuck in stop-and-go traffic stretching as far as he could see.

A sip of the still-warm coffee, and bite of the egg sandwich that he purchased on his way to the office each morning, always made the busy CEO's commute more tolerable, provided he didn't spill anything on himself as he continually maneuvered around all of the cars.

"Looks like another Ozone Action Day in the city," the radio blared, "and you know what that means. That's right. Free bus rides, at least for those of you who aren't too lazy to leave your personal vehicles at home!"

"Oh, come on, not another Ozone Day. That makes four in a row," another announcer complained.

"Yeah, four in a row, but who's counting?"

"Well, if you're not, you should be. Do you know the average person out in Los Angeles sits idle in traffic 82 hours per year? No wonder their air quality is worse than ours … and if you're not trying to do your part to cut down on air pollution, heck, any pollution for that matter, you should be. We all should."

Slamming on his brakes as traffic once again came to a standstill, Fred grimaced as he thought about what he'd heard on the radio.

Moments later, Jacobson's cell phone rang and the name "Martha Samuels" appeared on the phone's caller ID. "Strange. Why would my assistant be calling this early?" the CEO thought to himself as he answered the phone.

"Mr. Jacobson, I won't be able to come into the office today," Martha's voice sounded breathless and frightened as she spoke. "We're having an emergency with Sophie."

The CEO's concern grew as the sound of a siren could be heard in the background. "They're here. I've got to go." And the line went dead.

Fred thought about his assistant's 5-year-old daughter and what might have happened to her as he caught a glimpse of the downtown skyline, which seemed to punch its way through the brownish haze as if trying to get a breath of fresh air.

Guiding the vehicle into his parking space, Fred grabbed his briefcase, newspaper, the now-empty Styrofoam cup and sandwich container and walked briskly toward the building, absently throwing his trash into the container by the door. A quick trip on the express elevator brought him to the executive suite on the 40th floor.

As the CEO reached his office, he glanced in the direction of Martha's empty desk and made a mental note to call her before lunch to find out more about what happened to her daughter.

After the morning's meetings, he dialed Martha's cell phone, only to hear a recording. Leaving a message, he asked her to call if she needed anything, his concern growing about little Sophie.

Settling at his desk to begin paperwork, the CEO opened the morning's newspaper and immediately saw a headline containing the name of his company's largest competitor: "Stocks in downward spiral after spill pollutes community's sole drinking water source."

With a red pencil, he began underlining key phrases within each paragraph. Then, writing several of them on a pad of paper and reading down the list, the executive wrote the letters "N-I-M-B-Y" in bold letters, standing for "**N**ot **I**n **M**y **B**ack **Y**ard," and at that moment he vowed to do everything possible to create a culture that would prevent accidental pollution, a culture to preserve and nurture the planet.

Next, the CEO flipped to a clean page and wrote, "Our Culture of Environmental Stewardship." Then he drew four columns, labeling each with one of the following: "Air" – "Water" – "Waste" – "Conservation." He then began thinking about the impact his company's operations could or – worse yet – *had been* having on the environment. Taking a deep breath, he began writing them in the appropriate column.

Before leaving the office several hours later, Fred wrote some notes for his upcoming management team meeting:

> "The lack of a properly researched and well-thought-out company-wide effort to increase our environmental responsibility equals significant exposure to our financial performance and, conceivably, the future viability of the company.

"My goal: Make funds available and identify a person to spearhead this effort – someone knowledgeable of our operations, both foreign and domestic, as well as our culture, willing to help move environmental stewardship – from our minds to our hearts – where real change takes place."

Two days later, Fred Jacobson met with his senior management team to discuss his vision. "This isn't a knee-jerk reaction," he began, "as I think all of you are familiar with our competitor's problems after their recent spill."

There were nods of agreement around the table.

Ron Kaiser was the first to comment: "Aren't we already regulated up to our eyeballs? We've been doing business this way for decades. Never had a problem with the Environmental Protection Agency or the Bureau of Oceans or whatever they call themselves, so I don't see a need to spend time, money and resources on this environmental thing … and remember, we've been recycling shredded waste paper around here for years, so I think we're doing our bit."

"Stewardship," offered Martin Avery, the newest manager at the table. "It's called 'environmental stewardship,' and some companies are way ahead of the curve because they've made it a part of their core values. Honestly, we're lagging behind and that's concerning."

"Concerning?" Ron Kaiser hadn't expected to hear that word.

Avery was new to the group but not bashful in the least. "Yes, it's concerning because this awareness and willingness to help sustain the environment makes it easier to hire and retain top talent, not to mention capture additional market share," the young manager pointed out.

"Exactly," agreed the CEO. "Look how demonstrating and rewarding proper beliefs and behaviors helped us create our culture of safety versus just having periodic safety programs like we used to. While not hurting people would be enough for me, we've also been awarded additional contracts in both the Middle East and South America, all based on our safety performance. Morale is the highest it's ever been … and our productivity … well, you've seen the numbers, right, Kaiser?"

The man nodded.

"And, as you know, I'll be participating on that panel next week in Washington, D.C. That's about leading our industry," Fred reminded the group.

"But that's about safety – making sure our people get home every night to their families," Kaiser countered, beginning to realize his attitude about the environment may be in the minority.

"So, who says making sure we, as a company, don't harm the environment isn't just as important?" Fred asked the group.

Responding to the CEO's question, Avery replied as he turned toward Kaiser, "You're right, Ron. Safety means saving lives … or at least preventing injuries, but so does making certain we don't contribute to poor air quality or fouling a whole town's water supply. Without establishing high standards of environmental stewardship, we could easily kill hundreds, even thousands of people …."

"Let me help emphasize Avery's point," Fred continued. "I'm sure most of us around this table are old enough to remember hearing about the 1976 disaster in Seveso, Italy … caused when a plume of chemically contaminated vapors was released by a pesticide plant.[1]

---

[1] http://archive.unu.edu/unupress/unupbooks/uu21le/uu21le09.htm

More than 37,000 people were exposed to the highest levels of a dioxin, a class of chemicals believed to be highly poisonous and cancer-causing, even in micro-doses."

"I remember hearing about it," Kaiser admitted.

"Several thousand were treated for dioxin poisoning, more than 80,000 animals had to be slaughtered to keep the toxins out of the food chain," Fred explained, "and the data collected on the dioxin exposures are still under study."

"Data? What kind of data?" Kaiser asked, looking skeptical.

"Blood samples from the victims were saved," explained the CEO. "Today, thanks to technology, scientists can better quantify the damage. Moreover, the name 'Seveso' is now the name of a law, requiring every facility that handles quantities of hazardous materials – even if they're just storing it – to inform the authorities and people living near the plant about the hazards … plus this same law mandates that the plant develop and publicize ways for the community to respond to major incidents should another occur."

"But that was a chemical plant … in a country halfway around the world," Kaiser pointed out.

"So what?" challenged Avery. "Think about all of the hazardous materials our people use every day. Or the runoff some of our sites produce. And what if there was an explosion or fire at one of our locations near a town?" he added. "Look, Kaiser, even I understand the potential for disaster and I'm a newcomer here."

"Kaiser, it sounds to me like you still have some of your *bulletproof mentality* – thinking we've never suffered a major industrial incident after all the years we've been in business, so why should we expect to have one now," Fred said.

"Okay, okay, I know when I'm outnumbered," Kaiser responded, holding up his hands in mock surrender.

As the laughter around the table quieted, Jacobson continued. "So our next order of business is identifying someone to begin the process of changing our culture."

"If I may …" Avery interrupted. "In one of my last college courses, I read an article titled 'Leading Change: Why Transformation Efforts Fail' by John Kotter, Ph.D., a respected authority. Anyway, he listed eight stages we have to go through in order to transform our culture."

"Is this where you start telling us all of the things we're doing wrong according to some textbook?" Kaiser interrupted sarcastically. "That's exactly the reason some of us didn't want to go to college."

"Quite the opposite!" came Avery's somewhat defensive reply. "I was actually going to tell Fred we've already begun the process of changing the company's culture. 1)We've established an urgent reason for change; and 2)the people sitting at this table have the power to drive and lead that change. Next we'll need to create a clear vision and begin developing the strategies for achieving the vision."

"Oh good! Then we're 25 percent of the way there," Kaiser joked. "Sounds like we'll have this completed by dinner."

"I used the word 'process' for a reason," the CEO interjected to stop the banter. "I know this is not a program or an event, and it's going to take time to create a culture of environmental responsibility, or 'stewardship' as Avery called it. So let's get back to who can help us lead this transformation effort."

To everyone's surprise, Kaiser was the first to speak: "I think Kurt Bradshaw is that person. As everyone knows, because of the great job Kurt did helping change our safety culture, we recently promoted him from manager of worldwide safety to vice president of health, safety and environment, and, in his new role, he now reports to Fred."

"I can see the dramatic decline in our incident rates over the last 12 months," Avery said, "but being new with the company, I'm not familiar with what Kurt did."

Kaiser thought for a moment. "Well ... Kurt did a great job recognizing the old-school mindset and bulletproof mentality that kept everyone from seeing the need for change. He also helped our people understand those things they do that put them or someone else at risk – he called them at-risk behaviors – and are the root cause of most incidents. Come to think of it, I'll bet at-risk behavior, or people's behavior in general, is key when it comes to environmental stewardship."

The group sat in stunned silence at Kaiser's apparent insight. "What ... you don't think I see the similarities between creating a culture of safety and creating a culture of environmental stewardship? You show me a truly safe operation and I'll show you an environmentally responsible one. As I see it, they go hand-in-hand."

"Bradshaw's a great change manager and a good choice," Barbara Allen agreed. "He has the ability to translate our expectations of building a culture of environmental awareness, communicate that with our people and provide feedback in a positive manner that motivates people to want to change their behavior. He also demonstrated his obvious commitment to his team, which tells me he definitely has the necessary leadership skills."

"So, it appears Bradshaw's a unanimous choice. Am I right?" Fred asked as he glanced around the table. "If so, I'll meet with Kurt later this afternoon to give him the good news ...."

✦ ✦ ✦ ✦ ✦

Kurt arrived home that evening to share the news with his family. "Anybody home?" he called as he put down his briefcase.

"In the kitchen," answered his mother-in-law, Janet, who had just finished bundling the last of a stack of newspapers. "I'm on my way to the community recycling center," she said as she reached the front door. "Would you grab those two other bundles?"

Kurt picked up the newspapers and followed Janet to her car.

"This week ... paper, next week ... plastics," she called as she loaded the papers into her car. "There's always something that needs recycling ... always some way we can shrink our ecological footprint."

"Just drive carefully, Janet," Kurt waved. "If we're going to save this old planet, we're going to need all the environmentalists we can find."

"Environmentalist? I'm not sure I want to be called that!" the older woman exclaimed.

Looking surprised, Kurt asked, "What's wrong with being an environmentalist?"

"Well, nothing's wrong with a person taking responsibility for doing all they can to protect the air we breathe, water we drink, or land we use, but oftentimes people think of some crazy radical when they hear the word 'environmentalist' ... almost as if to say, 'Oh, you're one of *them*,'" Janet said.

"I agree. Movies about global warming and activists throwing paint on people's fur coats have caused an 'us-against-them' mentality," Kurt said, shaking his head. "I really just want you to know how much I appreciate you taking time to help our environment."

"You're sweet for saying that … but I've got to leave if I'm going to be home in time for dinner," she called out the window as she drove away.

Kurt was reading the newspaper stories that Fred Jacobson had shared while telling him about his new responsibility. Kurt shook his head in disbelief at the devastation detailed in the file and then looked back at the date of each clipping. Every incident had occurred during the last six months.

"Honey, where are you?" his wife, Jessica, called out.

"In here," Kurt responded.

"Oh, there you are," the pretty, dark-haired woman said as she entered the room. "Have a good day?"

Kurt stood and held out his arms. "Not sure yet," he said. "I was asked to take on a new responsibility … besides safety."

"No, don't hug me I'm sweaty from my run," she said, stepping out of reach and sitting down on the floor to stretch. "So what's this new responsibility and why aren't you sure about it?"

"One of our strongest competitors is dealing with lawsuits – big lawsuits – after a spill polluted an entire community's drinking water. From what I've read, I'm not sure the company will survive. Not that I would mind one less competitor, but the environmental disaster, in one way or another, impacts all of us.

"You mean your entire industry could be negatively impacted or we, as in 'our family,' could be hurt by the spill?"

"I knew I married a smart girl," Kurt joked, "but, actually, it's probably both. The spill will result in more regulations, which means more costs to the company and, ultimately, higher prices for the consumer since those costs will be passed along."

Listening intently, Jessica asked, "So what's your role in all of this?"

"Well, as the vice president of health, safety *and* environment, Fred wants me to work on establishing some high standards of environmental stewardship in our company's culture."

"Well, if what you did for the company's safety culture is any indication, they certainly have the right man for the job!" Jessica announced as she jumped up and hugged her husband.

"Yuck … talk about air pollution; I thought you were sweaty from your run!" Kurt teased, trying to keep his wife at arm's length.

"You'll just have to hold your breath," his wife countered. "I'll go shower before mom gets back and then the three of us can go eat dinner."

Once the dishes had been cleared, Kurt's wife asked, "So, how come when you got home this afternoon and I asked how your day was, you told me you weren't sure?"

After hesitating, Kurt began: "I know very little about environmentalism, except your mom taking things like paper, plastic, and aluminum cans to the recycling center every week. But, that's it … except for what I read in the paper or see in the news … and I have to admit, I haven't really paid much attention."

"Want to learn from an expert?" Janet piped up.

"Oh … no, Janet. I'm not joining your recycling group, if that's what you're suggesting."

The gray-haired woman frowned. "We wouldn't let you anyway," she said, winking. "No, I was thinking you might want to get to know my friend, Jim Corley … well actually, he's Dr. James Corley and I know he's spent much of his career studying and understanding the balance between environmental, social and economic issues. He's also someone I enjoy spending time with, sort of a nerd with a personality," she added, smiling.

Sensing her husband's apprehension, Jessica chimed in, "Might be good, just to talk with Jim. Remember how much Sam Rollins helped when you were working on creating a culture of safety for the company?"

Kurt nodded. "You're right. Sam was invaluable, and … I'm beginning to feel outnumbered here."

"You are," the two women acknowledged in unison.

"Hey, I have an idea." Jessica began smiling. "You know we have talked about getting a dog now that Shannon's in college. Why don't we get a little boy dog to even your odds?"

"And they have some wonderful puppies at the animal shelter," Janet added helpfully.

"Doggy recycling, is it?" Kurt joked. "Okay, okay. We'll think about a dog, but what I need right now is to get some sleep. It's been a long day and 'Captain Environmental' needs to get up early if he's going to save our planet from those evil polluters!"

Later that night, as he tossed and turned, Kurt recalled experiencing a similar feeling of dread when he had been asked to help improve the company's safety culture. He was confident in his knowledge of operations but wasn't sure he knew anything about safety.

"As we moved through that process, I learned that the leadership skills I used to achieve high operational performance were the same skills I needed to create a culture of safety. Can it be the same when it comes to the environment?" he wondered.

"And what we need to focus on are the things people have in common, relative to the environment, no matter what country they're from." He thought about that a moment longer. "We all want plenty of clean air and clean water, plus enough food and shelter," he said aloud, as Jessica lay sleeping peacefully by his side. "We all want to pass along a healthy planet to our children and grandchildren … at least that's what we say, but do our actions really demonstrate that?"

His mind went back to the article about their competitor's recent spill. "An entire town without clean water? I wonder if they had to haul in drinking water? What about water for the farmers in the area with their livestock and crops? How far did people have to travel to bathe and wash their clothes? And what about things like the value of people's homes and how much more they might have to pay for homeowners' insurance, or even their health insurance?"

"Wow! The consequences of this single incident could touch thousands of lives for years to come," he realized. "Creating a culture of environmental stewardship could be even more difficult than creating a culture of safety," he thought to himself.

Now fully awake, Kurt climbed out of bed and walked to his study. Thinking more about the steps that had been required to motivate "safety leaders" across the company, he took out a clean piece of paper and began to write:

- ✦ Build a foundation of trust.
- ✦ Set clear goals and high expectations.
- ✦ Praise progress when people begin changing behaviors.
- ✦ Have the courage to keep going.

"It looks easy on paper," Kurt observed before heading back to bed. "I guess I'll call Dr. Corley in the morning," he thought to himself. "I know with our operations running day and night, not to mention our shortage of personnel, we'll need an environmental process that our people will use both at work and at home, 24/7."

Snapshot

Definitions

1. **Behavior** – Our actions and mannerisms, day in and day out, as we relate with the environment … our response to various stimuli, whether internal or external, conscious or subconscious and voluntary or involuntary.
2. **Bulletproof mentality** – Thinking we won't hurt the environment as a result of our actions or behaviors.
3. **Culture** – The beliefs and behaviors transmitted from one generation to the next.
4. **Culture of Safety** – Every organization has a Safety Culture, which can range from poor to outstanding. A Culture of Safety implies safety has become a core value that is imbedded into every aspect of the organization's culture.
5. **Ecological footprint** – A measure of human demand on the Earth's ecosystems. It represents the amount of biologically productive land and sea area necessary to supply the resources a human population consumes, and to mitigate associated waste. Using this assessment, it is possible to estimate how much of the Earth it would take to support humanity if everybody followed a given lifestyle.
6. **Environment** – Refers to our surroundings, including all living and non-living things that occur naturally on Earth.
7. **Environmentalist** – A person who broadly supports the goals of the environmental movement, "a political and ethical movement that seeks to improve and protect the quality of the natural environment through changes to environmentally harmful human activities."

8. **Environmental stewardship** – Refers to responsible use and protection of the Earth's natural environment, through conservation and sustainable practices.
9. **Gyre** – In oceanography it is any large system of rotating ocean currents, particularly those involved with large wind movements.
10. **Incident** – A term used throughout this book, rather than Accident, because Accident implies something happened outside of someone's control, which is not the case more than 97 percent of the time.
11. **Old-school mindset** – The idea that because "we've always done things this way," there's no need to share our concerns ... or possibly consider a better way.
12. **Safety leader** – A person, at any level of an organization, whose beliefs and behaviors demonstrate their commitment to their own safety as well as the safety of those around them.
13. **Stewardship** – An ethic that embodies responsible planning and management of resources. The concept of stewardship is linked to the concept of sustainability.

STEPS TOWARD STEWARDSHIP

1. The changes we expect (our expectations) are at the core of building a culture of environmental stewardship and, at the same time, improving every aspect of operations.
2. People will elevate their work practices to the level of environmental protection and awareness that's expected, particularly if it benefits them, their families, the company and others.

Additional Activities

1. Research and write a 500-word paper on the Seveso, Italy, disaster. Find out about any additional environmental damage that occurred as a result of the accidental discharge of lethal gas. Look for agricultural impact, such as livestock, crops, and non-cultivated plants, such as trees, landscaping, etc. What about long-term impacts, such as health, economic and quality of life?
2. Determine the long-range extent of the Seveso disaster. In a 500-word paper, discuss the specifics of its impact.
3. Think about the impact of any accidental discharge into the air. Then write about a fictional incident/disaster in your hometown and how life would change as a result. 500 words should allow for plenty of "creative thinking."
4. Take a look at any three environmental disasters in your country over the past 100 years. From your study of these disasters, total the economic impact, including rebuilding, remediation, etc. Now, compare this to the amount of money spent to prevent similar situations from occurring. Report your findings in writing or through discussion.
5. In your own words, evaluate the environmental culture of your school, company or neighborhood. Are people, in general, aware of their environmental footprint (the environmental impact of their behavior)?

Resources

Environmentalism: A Global History, by Ramachandra Guha (1999)

Environmental Since 1945: The Making of the Contemporary World, by Gary Haq and Alistair Paul (2011)

The New Economy of Nature, by Gretchen Dailey and Katherine Ellison (2003)

Environmental Tips: Things You Can Do

Use Compact Fluorescent Bulbs

Replace light bulbs with compact fluorescent bulbs. By using three CFBs, you will save 300 lbs. of carbon dioxide and $60 a year.

Fill the Dishwasher

You don't have to run your dishwasher every time you eat. By filling it completely, you can save $40 and 100 lbs. of CO_2 emission a year.

Use Recycled Paper

By using 100 percent post-consumer recycled printer paper, you can save 5 lbs. of carbon dioxide per ream of paper. Don't forget to invest in recycled paper towels and napkins as well!

Adjust Your Thermostat

If you move your thermostat down 2 degrees in the winter and 2 degrees up in the summer, you can save up to $98 and 2,000 lbs. of CO_2 per year. Think of the warm sweater or cool bathing suit you can buy with that money.

Take Shorter Showers

Did you know that showers account for 2/3 of all water heating costs? We know – it's shocking. Cut your showers short and save $99 and 350 lbs. of CO_2 per year.

Carpool When You Can

With gas prices burning a hole in everyone's wallet, save some cash while saving 790 lbs. of CO_2 by carpooling. If your car is too small to fit all of your BFFs, then commute on public transportation or ride your bike.

Source: www.DoSomething.org

2 History Repeats Itself … Around the World

"Jim Corley," a friendly voice answered the phone.

"Dr. Corley," Kurt began. "My name is Kurt Bradshaw. We haven't met, but my mother-in-law, Janet Atkins, suggested you as a possible resource for a new project I'm working on."

"So Janet's your mother-in-law … you poor guy," Corley joked. "Actually, she's a great lady and a good friend." He paused. "So, how can I help with your project?"

As Kurt began explaining his new assignment, Corley grew more enthusiastic. "I love a challenge! What's your deadline?" the older man asked.

"I need to get started as soon as possible."

"Tomorrow morning soon enough?" Corley inquired.

"The sooner, the better!"

"How about 9:30 a.m.?"

"Sounds good," said Kurt, already comfortable with Janet's friend. "Where's the most convenient place for us to meet?"

"Let's start here at my house," the older man suggested.

"I'd like to bring Raj Singh, my project assistant, with me, if that's okay," Kurt said.

"No problem. The more, the better. I'll look forward to seeing you tomorrow morning."

As Kurt ended the call, he studied his cell phone before putting it back into his pocket. "Me, too, Dr. Corley. Me, too!"

Kurt hurriedly finished the apple he had been eating as he parked his car in Jim Corley's driveway the next day. He noticed the row of solar panels lining the roof of the Corley home as well as the rainwater collection barrels to one side.

"Looks like Dr. Corley practices what he preaches," Kurt said.

"It also looks like Dr. Corley knows how to do more using less," Raj commented.

The two were surveying the attractive, natural landscaping when the front door opened and a tall, slender man with white hair walked out to greet them.

"Kurt, I've heard so much about you and Jessica from Janet. Glad we're finally meeting," he said, extending his hand and offering a sturdy handshake.

"Janet's an amazing lady," Kurt said, "and, from my view, the world's greatest mother-in-law."

"And, as I said, she's also a good friend," the older man said, pausing a moment. Then, he turned to Kurt's assistant. "And you must be Raj. Glad you could come."

"Thank you for inviting me, Dr. Corley," the young man responded.

"Please, please. Call me Jim. But, let's go inside. I have an office where we can talk."

"You coffee drinkers?" Corley's voice interrupted Kurt's gaze around the room.

"Absolutely!"

Raj nodded his head.

"Okay. I'll be right back. Just put on a fresh pot," Corley called over his shoulder as he headed toward the kitchen.

"Great, thanks," Kurt replied absently as he noticed the photographs on the wall. There were pictures of huge fires and raging rivers bloated with flood waters. Others pictured what looked like debris-lined beaches ravaged by chemicals or other types of spills. "Looks like Jim has seen it all," he said.

"Yes, and some of these photos are quite familiar," Raj commented.

"So here's how I operate. I'll get your first cup of coffee. After that, you're free to help yourselves." Jim Corley's cheerful voice jolted Kurt out of his review of what looked to be a gaping, flaming hole in the ground.

"Oh, I see you found one of my favorites – a real hellhole, that one," Corley said, referring to what looked like nothing more than a giant firepit in the middle of the otherwise barren desert.

"Looks really strange. What is it?"

"Ever heard of the Darvaza crater?"[1] Corley asked without waiting for an answer. "Happened about 1971 after the ground beneath a drilling rig collapsed and opened a huge, poisonous gas cavern – about 100 meters wide. Geologists had hoped the fire would extinguish itself in a few days, but that never happened. Apparently allowing it to burn is safer and more environmentally friendly than releasing the methane, a relatively powerful greenhouse gas."[2]

"Wow! Since 1971?" Raj said, studying the photograph more closely. "That's crazy!"

"And costly, to say the least," Corley agreed, setting three cups of coffee between them. "Just an example of what can happen when we misuse and abuse this planet."

"Oh … oh yes. I understand," Kurt agreed although he had to admit, the words "misuse" and "abuse" hadn't come to mind when he looked at that photo.

"So, tell me more about your project," said the older man, glancing at his watch. "I want to make sure we have plenty of time, but I'm scheduled to leave for another appointment at noon."

"Oh sure, no problem. As I mentioned yesterday, I've been given additional responsibility – and I'm feeling a little overwhelmed right now, simply because I've never worked on a project involving

[1] www.businessinsider.com/turkmenistan-darvaza-gas-crater-2012-10?op=1
[2] www.businessinsider.com/turkmenistan-darvaza-gas-crater-2012-10?op=1

environmental stewardship," Kurt explained, downplaying the helplessness he felt. "So, I'm hoping you can tell us where to begin … because right now, we haven't a clue."

Corley chuckled. "You guys sound like me … about three decades ago."

Kurt recounted the earlier conversation he had with the CEO and what was expected from him in his new role. "Essentially, I've been asked to develop a strong company culture of environmental stewardship. This means a lifestyle change as well as changes in individual belief systems for our employees, not just here but around the world," Kurt explained.

Taking his time to respond, Corley said finally, "Well, I have to agree – there's a lot of ground to cover, moving from the way things are done today to your goal of becoming environmentally responsible. We're going to get people to believe their behavior can make a difference when it comes to reducing the way they misuse and abuse our water, air … heck, our entire planet, but I can promise you, nothing is impossible."

Kurt sat back, relaxing more as the conversation continued. "Thanks, I sure hope so! And I agree with you, helping people understand how their behavior can make a difference will be one of the most difficult issues … one I learned while I was working on changing people's at-risk behaviors."

"So, what are 'at-risk' behaviors?" Corley wanted to know.

"At-risk behaviors are things a person does, day in and day out, that put them or someone else at risk. They're the root cause of most incidents,"[3] Kurt responded.

"Makes sense. In fact, I recently read a study that said people's behaviors are the cause of incidents more than 88 percent of the time,[4]

[3] *Safety 24/7*. Anderson and Lorber. 2006
[4] www.asse.org/professionalsafety/pastissues/056/10/052_061_F2Manuele_1011Z.pdf

and I think you'll find that's the case when it comes to environmental incidents as well. Pick any man-made environmental disaster and I can show you how someone's behavior contributed to the incident!" Corley exclaimed confidently.

"Agreed," Kurt responded. "But it's often the company's culture that allows – and even influences – the way a person behaves."

"Okay. I'll agree with you on that. But just so we're on the same page, what do you mean when you use the word 'culture'?" Corley inquired.

"A company's culture is made up of group beliefs and behaviors that are transmitted from one generation to the next," Kurt said. "But, getting back to at-risk behaviors for a minute, they're also the foundation of what we call the 'safety pyramid.' Raj, you want to take Jim through it?" he asked, handing them copies.[5]

Corley studied the pyramid illustration. "Okay, help me. What does this illustrate?"

"The safety pyramid shows how an at-risk behavior can easily escalate to become anything from a 'near hit' to a 'fatality.' Our only control

[5] Anderson and Lorber

over the outcome is at the base of the pyramid when we choose to do, or allow, an at-risk behavior," Raj explained.

"Okay, that makes sense," Corley agreed. "But do you see how it's the same principle for environmental incidents? If a person doesn't stop to consider the impact of his at-risk behavior on the environment, the outcome is out of his control. Take the Exxon Valdez oil spill.[6] Do you think the Valdez captain stopped to consider whether (1) drinking alcohol on the day of his ship's scheduled departure, or (2) not being on the bridge and providing a proper navigation watch when the ship 'fetched up hard aground' on Bligh Reef would contribute to one of the worst environmental disasters in history?"[7]

"I'm sure he didn't. So, spilling 10.9 million gallons of oil, massive fines and cleanup costs should make it easy for our people to understand the potential environmental damage that could occur when they don't stop to consider the impact of their at-risk behavior," Kurt said, hoping he was right.

"One would hope so. But let's look at another far greater man-made environmental disaster and you tell me if the impact of the at-risk behaviors were considered."

Raj leaned forward. "'Greater than the Valdez?"

"Estimated to be 100 times worse," Jim responded. "On Dec. 22, 2008, in Kingston, Tenn., a retaining wall at an electric power-generating plant gave way, flooding the surrounding land with 80 acres of coal sludge, a byproduct of ash from coal combustion. Fifteen homes were destroyed and many more contaminated with arsenic, mercury and lead."[8] Corley's expression darkened as he spoke.

[6] www.valdezalaska.org/discover-valdez-history/valdez-history-exxon-valdez-oil-spill
[7] www.valdezalaska.org/discover-valdez-history/valdez-history-exxon-valdez-oil-spill
[8] www.sourcewatch.org/index.php/TVA_Kingston_Fossil_Plant_coal_ash_spill

"Once investigators began looking for the cause, they found the plant had repaired the wall and the wall had not been constructed correctly."[9, 10] Corley stopped again, shaking his head. "Unbelievable … a spill bigger than the Valdez."

"Incredible," Raj agreed.

"These statistics are mind-blowing: In just one year, the toxic materials from that power plant included 45,000 pounds of arsenic, 49,000 pounds of lead, 1.4 million pounds of barium, 91,000 pounds of chromium and I forget what else, but that stuff is known – well-known – to cause cancer, liver and brain damage, among other problems," Corley said, visibly more emotional.

"So, while people inspecting the damage were walking around in protective gear to guard against the various hazardous materials, plant officials were telling people living in the area they did not think the spill was toxic.[11] Well, that did it. A group of us went over to Kingston to warn the folks about the toxicity of the spill."[12]

"You sound pretty passionate," Kurt remarked.

"I probably do," Corley admitted, "because while we were trying to warn the people about the dangers of that spill, we were arrested … making us look like the bad guys when we were trying to protect the town," the older man said.

"Clean up, which was estimated to take four or more years at a cost of more than $1 billion, continues. It'll be years before we know the total impact of this spill." Corley's face brightened. "But this incident did shine a spotlight on the lack of coal ash regulation, and the EPA

[9] www.sourcewatch.org/index.php/TVA_Kingston_Fossil_Plant_coal_ash_spill
[10] www.knoxnews.com/news/2009/jun/26/report-four-factors-led-to-fly-ash-spill/
[11] www.cnn.com/2008/US/12/23/tennessee.sludge.spill/?iref=mpstoryview
[12] http://seattletimes.com/html/nationworld/2008558917_sludge25.html

began working on how to make those retention ponds safer."

"Sounds like a good first step," Kurt volunteered, "I'm also getting that it's not easy to get people to think about the environmental impact of their at-risk behaviors."

"Can I tell you about a disaster that affected my entire family?" Raj inquired.

"Let's hear it," invited Corley.

"Bhopal, the city where I grew up, was considered one of India's greenest cities for years," he began. "Union Carbide's Bhopal facility was part of India's Green Revolution,[13] created to increase the productivity of our crops because, at that time, pesticides were being used more and we were striving to become self-sufficient in the agriculture business."

"Go on," Kurt encouraged.

"One night in December 1984, 40 tons of methyl isocyanate (MIC) – a deadly chemical used in pesticides – escaped from the plant, killing more than 2,250 immediately. Another 20,000 died from gas-related diseases, not to mention the 558,000 who were injured.[14] I hadn't been born at the time, but my family said they were fortunate because they were visiting relatives in New Delhi. Sadly, many, many of my parents' age group suffered throughout their lives with damage to their eyes and lungs, as well as chronic illnesses.

"As you both probably know, this disaster was the result of a poorly maintained plant, human error and a total lack of knowledge about how to respond to this disaster," Raj continued, "and as you so rightly

[13] www.umich.edu/~snre492/lopatin.html
[14] http://news.bbc.co.uk/onthisday/hi/dates/stories/december/3/newsid_2698000/2698709.stm

point out, it isn't easy to get people to consider the outcomes. That was definitely the case in Bhopal."

Corley shook his head, "And it could have all been prevented."

"This disaster has affected several generations," Raj continued. "So many orphans and critically ill people trying to keep their families together and so many children are being born with birth defects, more than 10 times the national average … and poisons from the disaster continue to leach into the groundwater."[15]

"Hard to believe the cleanup was not properly conducted," Kurt said. "If people had just thought about what they were ignoring, weren't repairing or saw as 'no big deal.'"

"It's been my experience that getting people to think about the damage their at-risk behaviors could cause is about as easy as riding a bull – all you have to do is just stay on the bull," Corley chuckled.

"Unfortunately, motivating people to change their at-risk behaviors has a lot to do with the potential consequences that person may suffer as a result of their behavior. Take airplane pilots for example," he continued. "They used to have the attitude they were better and smarter than any of their crew."

"I think I've worked for a few people who must have been pilots in their former life," Kurt commented, rolling his eyes.

"I think we all have, but over time, pilots began to realize the potential consequences of not listening to their crew who, like pilots, are generally the first people to die in a crash," Corley said.

"I get it … the pilots were motivated to change their behavior because

[15] http://tvaraj.com/2012/05/29/the-aftermath-of-the-bhopal-disaster-december-3-1984/

the consequences could be so severe. But how is that different when it comes to the environment?" Kurt questioned.

"Let me use that pyramid of yours to illustrate my point," Corley said, drawing an upside-down pyramid. "There's a lot of talk these days about the impact of global warming.

"With that in mind, this pyramid is based on a survey of more than 2,000 adults who were asked, 'Who or what do you think global warming will harm?' Then they were given eight categories to choose from.[16] Conducted by George Mason University's Center for Climate Change Communication,[17] the survey reveals just 32 percent of Americans think global warming will harm them personally," Corley pointed out.

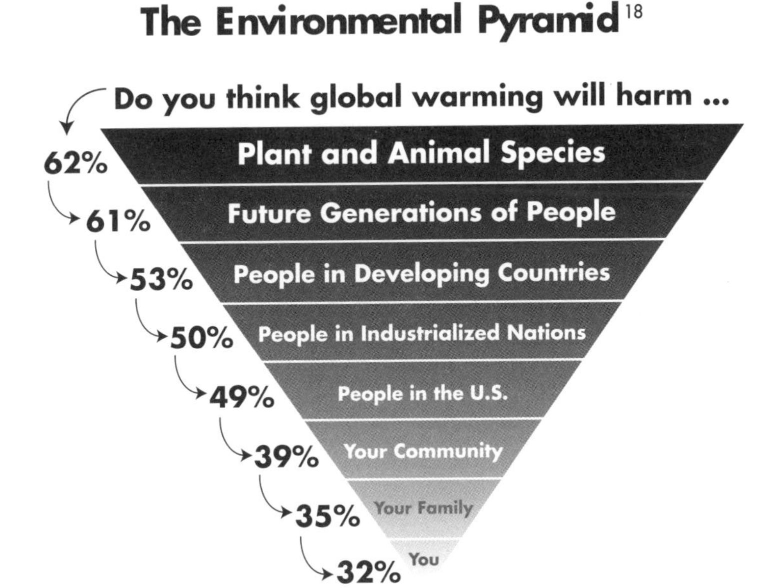

[16] http://environment.yale.edu/climate-communication
[17] www.climatechangecommunication.org/
[18] www.climatechangecommunication.org/

Kurt studied the Environmental Pyramid, his silence signaling a need for more information.

"The survey says people see climate change as something that's going to personally affect them the least …."[19]

"I get it," Kurt interrupted. "Unlike safety, where you understand your at-risk behavior could affect you most, when it comes to something like global warming, we don't really believe it will affect us so we're less motivated to change our behavior."

"Correct!" Corley confirmed, "but it's more than just individual behavior. This 'it's not going to affect me … or not going to happen in my backyard' attitude also makes it difficult for governments to push aggressively for new environmental policies or initiatives."

"Like what?"

"The Polluter Pays Principle,[20] for one."

"I've heard of that, but I'm not totally sure of what it involves," Raj was the first to admit.

"I could use a little help here, too," Kurt added.

"The Polluter Pays Principle, which is referred to as the PPP, is an environmental policy principle requiring the costs of pollution be paid by those causing it," Corley began.

"Sounds fairly straight forward," Raj remarked. "So, has it worked?"

"Well, the immediate goal was to factor the costs of pollution and environmental cleanup into the prices of goods and services as part

---

[19] www.climatechangecommunication.org
[20] www.guardian.co.uk/environment/2012/jul/02/polluter-pays-climate-change

of the costs to produce them," Corley continued, "but, like many good ideas, it looked more effective on paper than in real-world applications."

Kurt frowned. "So, are you saying it hasn't been effective?"

"Not totally," said Corley, "but it is a principle of international law ... which is one small step for the environment. However, as with more international laws, the difficult part is getting buy-in from the various nations. In the case of Polluter Pays, it's a fundamental principle of environmental policy for both the Organization for Economic Cooperation and Development (OECD) and the European Community.

"Unfortunately, it has been difficult, even though PPP has been around since the '70s," he continued, "and there's always been a bit of a rift in how people feel about assigning *responsibility* for cleanup, even if we have a common idea of who ought to be held *accountable.*

"Let me illustrate what I'm saying: Here's ABC Factory that produces waste – at any and all worksites. Are you with me?"

The two men nodded.

"So, this should be a no-brainer, right? The factory hires a company to haul the waste away and, in doing so, transfers responsibility for the waste to that hauler. But let's say the waste hauler dumps it illegally and then goes out of business. Who now is the accountable party?"

The men looked confused.

"So, would it be accurate to say ABC Factory is accountable for its own waste removal, but it is not directly responsible for the actual job of taking care of the waste since they've contracted another company to do that? This is a case where the responsible party and the accountable party are separate. But should they be?"

"I'm still confused," Kurt admitted.

"You gentlemen are like many environmental advocates today. Some interpret the Polluter Pays Principle in a way that demands that polluters specifically reduce their emissions – that is, that accountability and responsibility both belong to the polluter. But, there also are those who see the parties as different and have a difficult time deciding who should pay."

"So what seemed fairly easy to understand is really more complex than it looks," Raj surmised.

"Exactly right," Corley smiled, "and the other confusing part is determining how much the pollution cleanup will cost."

"Aha! Now I see why we haven't heard much about the PPP," Kurt reasoned.

"And we haven't talked about what happens in the case of accidental pollution … or exactly how we should determine what the polluter would pay," Corley added.

"So, we have PPP with a lot of good intentions but no real power to achieve the goals it was meant to achieve," Kurt figured out. "So, where do larger countries around the world stand on keeping the environment healthy?"

"Well, there are several countries miles ahead of us in their anti-pollution efforts as well as in policies to slow down pollution," explained Corley.

"Oh really," Kurt leaned closer. "But I thought the U.S. was one of the leaders in environmental stewardship."

"Not according to the 2012 Environmental Performance Index,"[21] Corley said, walking to his desk and picking up a folder. "I made copies in case you two hadn't seen the report."

Kurt scanned the pages. "Hmmm. It's ranking 132 countries in 22 areas of performance, and the 10 policy categories used in the rankings were:

- Environmental Health
- Water (effects on human health)
- Air Pollution (effects on human health)
- Air Pollution (ecosystem effects)
- Water Resources (ecosystem effects)
- Biodiversity and Habitat
- Forests
- Fisheries
- Agriculture
- Climate Change

"Based on the research, the strongest performers were Switzerland, Latvia, Norway, Luxembourg and Costa Rica. The U.S. isn't even in the Top Ten," he said, sounding surprised.

"This index measures two core objectives of environmental policy," the older man explained. "One is environmental health – the stresses caused by the environment on human health. The second is ecosystem vitality – ecosystem health and natural resource management."

"So what is Switzerland doing at the top of this list?" Raj asked.

[21] http://epi.yale.edu/

"Good question," Corley smiled. "If you've ever visited Geneva, for example, you couldn't help but notice ample clean water, the lack of heavy industry, numerous reforestation programs and lots of protected nature areas … and if you asked, the locals would probably be happy to tell you about their good national health care and an abundance of clean geothermal power. And, from a 'cultural' perspective, there is huge public awareness about maintaining a sustainable environment.

"Iraq, one of the bottom five, is there because of its deteriorating environment, thanks to ongoing wars between the sects.[22]

"Like most impoverished countries, Iraq lacks some of the most basic environmental amenities as well as the capacity for environmental policies … and the reason the U.S. was well below other industrialized countries, like the U.K., Germany and France, is because of air pollution and greenhouse gas emissions," Corley said. "Ultimately, the U.S., which has moved up to 49th from 61st in the 2010 survey,[23] has to step up even more how they address pollution control and natural resource management challenges."

"Okay, I get it," said Raj. "Germany and Switzerland as well as France – these countries rely more on public transportation, bikes and walking, so they don't have the pollution that we have, right?"

"Well, they're not pollution free," Corley interjected. "The exception to your theory is China, a country still using a lot of bicycles and ranked 100th. But we can say the higher-scoring countries enacted ways to protect the environment and may be more environmentally conscious than countries ranked lower down the scale.

"Yet, while not known for their environmental friendliness, China

[22] http://environment.yale.edu/news/article/switzerland-ranks-at-top-of-2012-environmental-performance-index/

[23] www.ciesin.columbia.edu/documents/EPI_2010_report.pdf

made it illegal for store owners to give out plastic bags for free in 2008, which has kept more than a billion bags out of landfills and cut bag consumption by 50 percent."[24]

"Here's another survey that showed Americans favored the environment over the economy 67percent to 28 percent in 2000, but in 2011, Americans favored the economy over the environment 54 percent to 36 percent, which appears to illustrate that during difficult economic times, environmental policies and initiatives get left behind,"[25] Corley said.

Kurt groaned. "Let me guess, it's the same in business."

Corley nodded. "Unfortunately, with a lot of organizations, environmental responsibility can appear to take a backseat to profitability, with sometimes devastating consequences. For example, in 1999, workers at a nuclear fuel factory in Tokaimura, Japan,[26] were preparing nuclear fuels and mixed uranium oxide with nitric acid using a stainless steel container instead of the proper mixing apparatus. This resulted in a nuclear chain reaction that killed two people and led to the temporary evacuation of 300,000 people around the plant. Later, it was determined a stainless steel tank was likely used as an attempt to save costs in order to be more competitive with foreign fuel suppliers."

"Which is why, just like safety, organizations need to make environmental responsibility one of their core values … because while priorities – like cost savings – can change, core values always remain the same," Kurt said. "Mind if I grab more coffee?"

"Right behind you," the older man replied. "What about you, Raj? Ready for more?"

---

[24] www.nytimes.com/2008/01/09/world/asia/09iht-plastic.1.9097939.html
[25] www.gallup.com/poll/146681/americans-increasingly-prioritize-economy-environment.aspx
[26] www.world-nuclear.org/info/Safety-and-Security/Safety-of-Plants/Tokaimura-Criticality-Accident/

With cups refilled, the three men resumed their conversation. "Back when I was working on the company's safety culture," Kurt began, "I learned to look beyond an individual's or group's actions to determine the attitude causing the behavior … for example, buckling your seatbelt every time you get into a car. Do you do it because it will keep you safe … or is it because you can get fined if you don't use your seatbelt and the police stop you?"

"I see your point, but why is it important to understand a person's motivation for behaving certain ways?" Corley wanted to know.

"Let me share something about a person's commitment and how important it is, whether developing a culture of safety or environmental responsibility," Kurt said, pulling out a piece of paper.

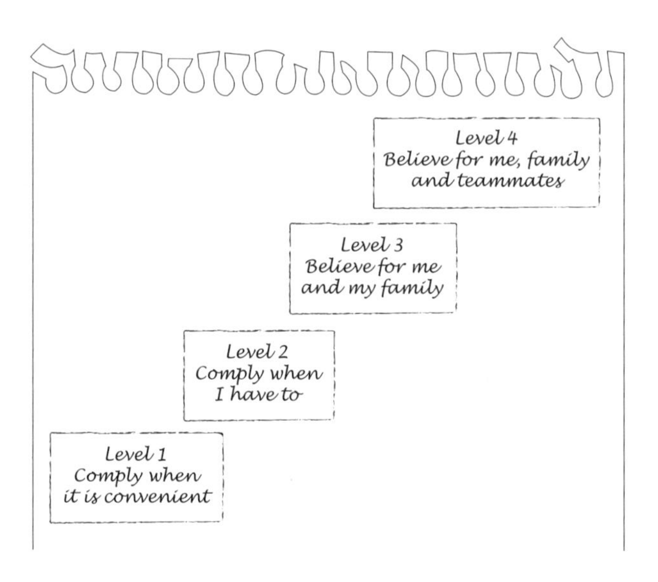

Kurt handed copies to Corley and Raj as he began to explain. Level 1 and 2 say, *Comply* – meaning I do it because I'm told, forced or paid to do it. At Levels 3 and 4, the attitude changes to *Believe* – meaning I made a conscious choice and am totally committed to working in that mindset. And here's the important part: I choose to work safely or environmentally responsibly whether anyone, including my boss, is watching or not."[27]

"So you're always demonstrating what a strong culture of safety *and* environmental responsibility looks like," Corley said, confirming his understanding.

"That's right. We create our culture by what we demonstrate as well as what we reward and tolerate in others," he said, "and we found the goal is to create an environment that *motivates* and *continually supports* a person's desire to move from Level 1 or 2 to a Level 3 or 4," said Kurt.

"Kind of like ***E***nvironment equals ***M***y ***C***ommitment and ***C***orporate's, or ***E*** = ***MC***^{2}," Raj added with a smile.

"Well stated!" Kurt replied.

"So, let's talk more about Levels of Commitment," Corley continued. "I want you to think about what your company rewards and/or tolerates from an environmental standpoint."

Kurt scratched his head thoughtfully. "Hmmm. I know there must be something."

Corley waited before he spoke again. "Let me give you some help."

"Looks like I need it," Kurt admitted, glancing at his assistant. "What about you?"

"Absolutely. This is new to me, too," Raj admitted.

"Well, Kurt, I wouldn't want to make this illustration too personal, but didn't I see you munching on something when you got out of the car this morning?"

[27] Anderson and Lorber, *Safety 24/7*

Looking slightly embarrassed, Kurt replied. "Uh, yes, I was eating an apple on the way over. Didn't have time to eat anything earlier."

"Don't worry. I'm not going to ask what level of safety commitment eating while driving represents, but would you mind going out to your car and getting what's left of your apple, as well as any other trash you might have?"

Puzzled, Kurt went outside and opened the door of his car. There, between the seats, was an apple core, paper towel and two empty plastic water bottles he and Raj had finished on their way to Corley's. Collecting everything, he returned back inside the house, wondering what Corley planned to do with all this trash.

"Okay, let's see what we have here," said Corley as he picked up the apple core by its stem. "Whenever I have anything organic left over, I always put it in my compost pile," the older man smiled, "and as far as these empty plastic bottles go, do you only drink bottled water?"

"Guilty as charged," Kurt admitted. "In fact, we probably go through a couple of cases at home every week … maybe more."

"Same goes for me," said Raj.

"I don't know what you do with your empty bottles, but Kurt here is lucky enough to have his mother-in-law, Janet, taking care of recycling his plastic bottles."

"Uh, yes. I'll need to give her an extra hug when I get home this afternoon," Kurt laughed, "but doesn't recycling cost money?"

"Sure it does," Corley said, "but according to the Natural Resources Defense Council and the U.S. Environmental Protection Agency, 'a well-run curbside recycling program can cost anywhere from $50 to more than $150 per ton. Disposal programs, on the other hand, cost anywhere from $70 to more than $200 per ton.' This tells us, while there's still room for improvement, recycling can be cost-effective.[28, 29]

"More importantly, have you considered purchasing a filter so you can drink water from the faucet?" Corley continued. "Not only would you eliminate the need to dispose of empty bottles, you also save the natural resources required to manufacture the bottle in the first place.

"Let me tell you about the bigger picture when it comes to your water bottles," he said, looking at the plastic bottles Kurt had brought in. "Only 13 percent of water bottles are recycled.[30] Does that number surprise either of you?"

The two guests nodded their heads.

"So, here's more shocking news," Corley said. "In 2005, Americans purchased 30 billion water bottles, and 26 billion of them wound up in landfills ... and to round out the picture, according to *National Geographic*, Americans drink more bottled water than any other nation. Making all of those bottles uses 17 million barrels of crude oil annually. That is equivalent to the fuel needed to keep 1 million vehicles on the road for 12 months.[31]

"Okay, I'm a little slow, but I think I'm finally getting it. This environmental stewardship covers much more of our landscape than I first thought," Kurt said.

"Indeed," Corley agreed. "It involves everything we do or don't do, from the time we get up in the morning to whenever we lay down at

[28] www.nrdc.org/cities/recycling/recyc/chap3.asp
[29] www.nrdc.org/cities/recycling/gsteps.asp
[30] http://greenliving.nationalgeographic.com/water-bottle-pollution-2947.html
[31] http://greenliving.nationalgeographic.com/water-bottle-pollution-2947.html

night. Like, for instance, what kinds of pillows we choose, what kinds of bedding we use and so on. You get the picture. It's with us 24/7."

Kurt looked at his watch. "I know you're on a tight schedule, but I just have one more question to ask."

"Go ahead. I've got time for one … even two questions," Corley smiled.

"Earlier we talked about demonstrating environmental stewardship," Kurt began. "So, how do I … how do you … ?"

"When you drove up today, you probably saw my rainwater collection system and the solar panels," the older man replied. "Even planting a tree, taking shorter showers and inflating tires can make a difference. Those are a few things I do to demonstrate my commitment to taking care of the environment … and, as Janet will tell you, I'm always looking for more ways to reduce, reuse, recycle and restore items. But, I also demonstrate my attitude toward the environment by speaking up, or educating people, if I see behaviors that could harm or put our environment at risk, just like I did with your apple core and water bottles."

"Just like with safety," Raj remarked, "but that takes courage, right?"

"Sure it does, which is why it is so important for companies to create a culture of trust that encourages and motivates people to speak up," Corley responded.

"So, like my mother-in-law, Janet, you've made environmental stewardship a habit?"

"It's one of my better habits," the older man grinned. "Yes, sometimes people give me strange looks, but I know a healthier planet begins with a personal commitment."

"So again, just like creating a culture of safety, environmental stewardship takes my commitment as well as a commitment from the company?"

"Yep, ***E = MC²***. You're picking up on this quickly," Corley said.

"You've given me so much to think about. Can we meet again … soon?"

"Does this same time next week work for you guys?"

"Great! Raj and I will both be here, and thanks, Jim, for making me think about the impact one person can have on the environment … and how if one person starts the ball rolling and is an example for others, we can soon make a gigantic difference!"

Corley then held up the two empty, plastic water bottles. "I'll recycle these," he said as he turned around and reached into a cabinet. "In trade, I'll give you one of these reusable water bottles. If you would, try and keep track of how many times you refill the bottles during the next week. Then let me know the number."

"That will be interesting," Raj acknowledged.

"Every time you refill the bottle will help you remember environmental stewardship is a habit. The other thing I want to emphasize – and this is the important part – what you've learned today might be in your head, but now you've got to move it to your heart, so you will use your hands to make a difference," he said, putting his hand on Kurt's shoulder. "Head, heart and hands …" Corley repeated as he walked Kurt and Raj to their car.

SNAPSHOT

DEFINITIONS

1. **At-risk behaviors:** Those actions we take, day in and day out, that put us or our environment at unnecessary risk.
2. **Company culture** – Made up of group behaviors and beliefs that are transmitted from one generation to the next.
3. **$E = mc^2$** – A formula for creating a corporate culture of environmental stewardship. **E** = environment; **m** = my commitment; **c** = corporate's commitment (these two commitments – my own and corporate's – bring commitments to the second power (C^2).
4. **Environmental sustainability** – Sustainability is based on a simple principle: Everything that we need for our survival and well-being depends, either directly or indirectly, on our natural environment. Sustainability creates and maintains the conditions under which humans and nature can exist in productive harmony, that permit fulfilling the social, economic and other requirements of present and future generations.
5. **Head, heart and hands** – Becoming an environmental steward requires a personal commitment, beginning with (1) an intellectual understanding of the risks (head), followed by (2) a commitment to making a positive difference and changing certain behaviors (heart), and (3) transforming this commitment into a habitual behavior (hands).
6. **Plastic water bottles** – According to the Beverage Marketing Corp., the average American consumed 1.6 gallons of bottled water in 1976. In 2006, that number jumped to 28.3 gallons. More than 2.4 billion pounds of plastic bottles were recycled

in 2008. Although the amount of plastic bottles recycled in the U.S. has grown every year since 1990, the actual recycling rate remains steady at around 27 percent. Recycling 1 ton of plastic saves 7.4 cubic yards of landfill.

7. **Polluter Pays Principle:** In environmental law, the Polluter Pays Principle is enacted to make the party who is responsible for producing pollution be responsible for paying for the damage done to the natural environment.

8. **The four R's** – Reduce, Reuse, Recycle and Restore – are at the heart of the "simple things you can do for the earth" movement. These concepts stretch into all areas of our life. We know it can be tough to change habits, especially when we are bombarded with messages to buy more and try the latest, greatest convenience fad. But intuitively we know that using something once and tossing it into the trash is wasteful.

Steps Toward Stewardship

1. Every human activity carries with it some type of risk to the health of the environment.
2. Each individual chooses his/her attitude toward taking care of the environment … or not.
3. Everyone is a blend of the four levels of commitment to environmental stewardship. So, which level do you practice most frequently?
4. We create our culture by what we demonstrate personally and what we reward and tolerate in others.
5. A strong culture of environmental stewardship begins when we make taking care of the environment a habit.
6. Creating environmental awareness is not only a personal issue but also a corporate one.

ADDITIONAL ACTIVITIES

1. Find articles on plastic pollution of our ocean gyres, such as the "Great Pacific Garbage Patch." How did it happen and what does it mean, globally, to the Earth's inhabitants?
2. In this chapter, the Polluter Pays Principle has been mentioned. Research it thoroughly and create a month-by-month or year-by-year timeline – from its origins to its current status.
3. Find articles on cities or towns across the globe that have begun to limit or ban plastic water bottles and/or plastic grocery bags. Why has this become an issue? Discuss what your hometown has done to limit slow-degrading plastic waste.
4. In your experience, what incentives have retailers offered in your area to reduce, reuse and recycle? Be specific about the incentives and other initiatives you find.
5. Select any man-made environmental disaster and report on the human behavior that led to the disaster.

RESOURCES

Five Past Midnight in Bhopal: The Epic Story of the World's Deadliest Industrial Disaster, by Dominique Lapierre and Javier Moro (2002)

Advocacy After Bhopal: Environmentalism, Disaster, New Global Orders, by Kim Fortun (2001; paperback)

The Bhopal Tragedy: What Really Happened and What It Means for American Workers and Communities at Risk, by M. Arun Subramaniam and Ward Morehouse (1986)

To read more about India's Green Revolution, go to www.npr.org/templates/story/story.php?storyId=102944731

Popular Mechanics: What Went Wrong: Investigating the Worst Man-Made and Natural Disasters, by William Hayes and the Editors of Popular Mechanics (May 3, 2011)

Nuclear Roulette: The Truth About the Most Dangerous Energy Source on Earth, by Gar Smith, Ernest Callenbach and Jerry Mander (Oct. 25, 2012)

Accident prone.(analysis of the accident at the Tokaimura nuclear facility in Japan): An article from: Bulletin . . . by Edwin Lyman and Steven Dolley (July 28, 2005)

The Economics of Waste, by Richard C. Porter. 2002

Gone Tomorrow: The Hidden Life of Garbage, by Heather Rogers. 2006

Waste and Want: The Social History of Trash, by Susan Strasser. 2000

Cradle to Cradle: Remaking the Way We Make Things, by William McDonough and Michael Braungart. 2002

Natural Capitalism: The Next Industrial Revolution, by Paul Hawken, Amory Lovins and L. Hunter Lovins. 2008

www.expatify.com/news/top-10-most-environmentally-friendly-nations.html

www.gallup.com/poll/146681/americans-increasingly-prioritize-economy-environment.aspx

Environmental Tips: Things You Can Do

Reduce Garbage
Recycle paper, plastic and glass, and buy products with less packaging. This can save 1,000 lbs. of carbon dioxide a year.

Plant a Tree
Show off your gardening skills and start planting. A single tree will absorb a ton (that's 2,000+ lbs.) of CO_2 over its lifetime.

Wash Your Clothes on the Cold Water Cycle and Air Dry
Because the water isn't being heated, you'll save energy. Air-drying your clothes will save 700 lbs. of CO_2 and up to $75 a year.

Ditch the Plastic
Plastic bottles are biodegradable and can sit in landfills for over 200 years! With 2.5 million plastic water bottles thrown away every hour in the U.S., it is best to start using a reusable water bottle.

Source: www.DoSomething.org

Air: Setting Goals for a Culture of Environmental Awareness & Action

After visiting with Jim Corley, Kurt was not only ready to dive into how to put the company on track toward greater environmental stewardship, but he also was motivated to do whatever he could to increase environmental awareness.

Kurt shared his concerns with his mother-in-law, Janet, and wife, Jessica, that night at dinner, citing the Yale University 2012 Environmental Performance Index and the low ranking that the U.S. had earned, which he found troubling.

"Well, it seems pretty obvious," said Jessica. "People think they can keep cluttering up the environment and polluting our air and water and nothing will change."

"But it has. It has changed," Kurt interrupted.

"I have friends who make fun of my recycling, so I know they either don't understand or, worse yet, care little about the stress we've all placed on our environment," Janet sighed.

"Well, at least schools are beginning to teach something about the environment. Although, I recently read an article about how teachers said making climate change fit their curriculum was the biggest challenge in 2007, but today their greatest concern is the controversy surrounding the cause of global warming,"[1] Jessica pointed out.

The conversation died off and everyone became lost in their own thoughts of what the future might hold. Janet broke the silence after glancing at her watch. "I would normally wish you both 'sweet dreams,' but after this conversation, I'm not sure whether to just say 'goodnight' or 'good luck.'"

The next morning, Kurt was eager to get to work.

"You going to stop and pick up something for breakfast on the way?" his wife asked.

"Nope. I'm beginning a new habit," he announced, taking two pieces of toast from the toaster. "I'm making my environmental footprint smaller, first by taking my favorite coffee mug to work … so no more Styrofoam cups needed. Second, I'm going to fill this reusable bottle that Jim Corley gave me.

Jessica listened, crossing her arms over her chest. "And what about your toast, Mr. Environmental Man?"

"Well, uh. Any suggestions, oh wise one?"

"Here's a plastic plate," Jessica offered. "Bring it home and you can use it again tomorrow."

[1] http://articles.latimes.com/2012/jan/16/nation/la-na-climate-change-school-20120116

Driving down the freeway, Kurt felt good about reducing his environmental footprint.[2] "I knew in my mind it was the right thing to do but I didn't expect to actually feel good about changing my behavior," he said to himself, "but I guess, just like safety, you have to move it from your head to your heart and on to your hands for real behavior change to take place."

It was early and few people were at their desks. However, as Kurt sat down, the company's CEO, Fred Jacobson, knocked at his door. "Good morning, Mr. Jacobson," a surprised Kurt said. But what surprised Kurt even more was the CEO's uncharacteristically disheveled appearance. Jacobson looked as though he had slept in his clothes, but the dark circles beneath bloodshot eyes made Kurt wonder if the CEO had even slept at all.

"Sorry to interrupt your morning … but I need to speak with you," Jacobson began somberly.

"I was just getting started," Kurt stammered. "But if I may Mr. Jacobson, are you okay?"

"No, not really … it was a very long and emotional night," came Jacobson's soft reply. "My executive assistant's 5-year-old daughter Sophie died last night. They had rushed her to the hospital with an acute asthma attack. It was the third one this year. They thought her condition was under control, but I guess they were wrong … her funeral is on Friday."

"I'm so sorry. Is there anything I can do to help?" Kurt wanted to know.

"Actually, you already are doing something," the CEO replied. "The doctors aren't sure what triggered the asthma attack, but they think

[2] http://www.footprintnetwork.org/en/index.php/gfn/page/calculators/

her condition was aggravated by the ozone action days[3] we had last week. So I want you to redouble your efforts to create a culture of environmental responsibility for us all … and I'm going to ask Martin Avery to stop by your office to discuss how he might be able to help you."

"That would be great, I really appreciate you making Martin available," Kurt replied.

Turning to leave the office, Jacobson's voice grew stronger. "Well, if ever we needed a reason to help reduce pollution, we have one now … and her name was Sophie."

Kurt sat quietly for a moment, thinking about his own daughter, Shannon, who was away at college. "Asthma, who would have thought," Kurt said to himself. Turning to his computer, Kurt typed www.aaaai.org and began to read:

- ✦ Asthma was linked to 3,447 deaths (about 9 per day) in 2007.
- ✦ More than half (53 percent) of people with asthma had an asthma attack in 2008. More children (57 percent) than adults (51 percent) had an attack. 185 children and 3,262 adults died from asthma in 2007.
- ✦ The number of people diagnosed with asthma grew by 4.3 million from 2001 to 2009.
- ✦ Annual expenditures for health and lost productivity due to asthma are estimated at over $20 billion. Medical expenses associated with asthma increased from $48.6 billion in 2002 to $50.1 billion in 2007.

Kurt was still reading when Raj stopped by on the way to his office. "You're here early. How's it going this morning?"

[3] http://en.wikipedia.org/wiki/Ozone_Action_Day

"Not well," Kurt answered in a somber voice. He told Raj of Sophie's death, as well as some of the statistics he had just finished reading.

"I know it's tragically ironic, but look at this story I read from an English newspaper, *The Guardian*," Raj said, handing the article to Kurt. The headline was astonishing: "UK Air Pollution Causes 55,000 Early Deaths a Year."[4] He read further:

"According to a six-month study by the environment audit committee, minute sooty particles, emitted largely from the burning of diesel and other fuels and inhaled deeply into the lungs, shortens lives by seven to eight months. In pollution hotspots, like areas of central London and other cities, the particles could be cutting vulnerable people's lives short by as much as nine years," the newspaper read.

Kurt shook his head in disbelief. "I had no idea," he said before looking back at the newspaper article Raj had given him:

"Long-term air pollution, from the sooty particles known as PM10s, nitrogen dioxide (NO2) and nitrogen oxides (NOx), makes asthma worse and exacerbates heart disease and respiratory illness."

"Well, after my conversation with Mr. Jacobson this morning, I can tell you the need for environmental stewardship is no longer NIMBY (Not In My Back Yard)," Kurt exclaimed.

"What do you mean?" asked Raj.

"Mr. Jacobson wants us to step up our efforts to make the company more environmentally responsible," Kurt elaborated. "Martin Avery's going to devote time to the project as well. I also think we need to spend time in Bhopal," he continued. "What better place to learn about what can happen when our air becomes deadly to breathe?"

[4] http://www.guardian.co.uk/environment/2010/mar/22/air-pollution-deaths

"I … I suppose there are a few areas where the people may have changed their habits," Raj replied, thinking of his devastated homeland.

Kurt took a sip from his new metal water bottle.

"Oh, I see you're using the bottle Dr. Corley gave us, too," Raj commented. "I've already filled mine three times this morning."

"That reminds me, I'm going to suggest that Dr. Corley travel with us to India. I think his environmental expertise will add a lot," Kurt added."Since you're familiar with the country, can you start looking at flights, hotels, etc.? If it's okay with you, I'd also like to spend a little time with your family, as I'm sure we'll be able to learn a few things from the experiences they've gone through."

"I'll start making some preliminary arrangements," Raj confirmed, looking at his watch. "It's early evening in India, so I'll give my parents a quick call as well."

"Thanks," Kurt replied. "But Raj, we need to be here on Friday for Sophie's funeral …."

✦ ✦ ✦ ✦ ✦

"Hey. Got a minute? Mr. Jacobson sent me."

Kurt looked up from his reading. "Sure. You must be Martin. Come in, come in," Kurt said.

Martin Avery looked very young but, as Kurt and Raj would soon learn, he was very impressive with a tremendous amount of knowledge about change management.

"I mentioned something about John Kotter's philosophy regarding change management in one of our meetings," he began, "and Mr.

Jacobson thought Dr. Kotter's approach might help accelerate a change in the company's environmental culture."

"Dr. Kotter was one of my professors at Harvard," Avery continued. "And I can tell you, his systematic approach to making changes in organizational culture[5] has been proven over the last couple of decades in many different industries. Here's the system he developed."[6]

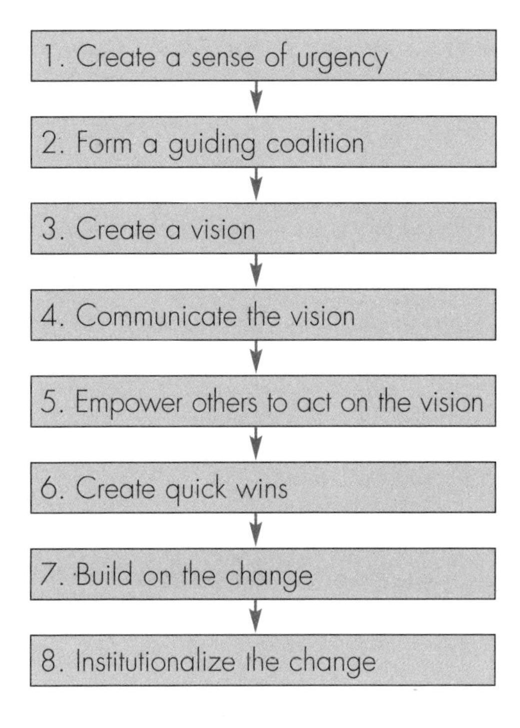

"So, where do we start?" Kurt asked eagerly. "Sounds like I have a lot to learn."

"Well, as I told Mr. Jacobson during our meeting last week, it appears we've already made good progress."

Kurt leaned forward. "How so?"

---

[5] www.kotterinternational.com/our-principles/changesteps/changesteps
[6] www.kotterinternational.com/our-principles/changesteps/changesteps

"According to Dr. Kotter, we've already begun the process of changing our culture. (1) We've already established an urgent reason for change; (2) Mr. Jacobson assembled the senior management team to focus on the issue; and (3) we created the vision, which you now have the power to lead and drive the change," Avery explained.

"Sounds good to me," Kurt replied enthusiastically.

"I've brought several copies of Kotter's process, and this will give you a good overview. But a key thing Kotter found is that most major change initiatives are, in reality, a series of smaller projects that go through Kotter's eight-step process. So, at any one time, while you might be halfway through your overall effort, you could also be finishing up a smaller project and just beginning another," said Avery. "Take the third step for example: We've established the vision and now you're working on developing the strategies for achieving it."

"Sort of like a story within a story?" asked Kurt.

"Exactly … and, in the process, you make a very large undertaking manageable for the organization by achieving milestones along the way and having pride in those accomplishments," the younger man said.

"One thing I learned when I was leading the effort to improve safety was that culture change is never easy. You are asking people to change the way they've been doing things for years. The old culture will fight it at every opportunity," said the vice president.

Avery smiled. "Agreed, which is why you need the small successes along the way."

"These 'successes' also help those people who support the change," Kurt added.

Avery nodded. "But tell me more about what you mean."

"Well, it helps people in two ways: First, people supporting environmental stewardship, as an example, are the champions you want and need to stay on board. Without some success along the way – like with smaller projects – early supporters become discouraged because they're the ones on the front lines, taking all the flak from the people who don't want to change. Secondly, the more success there is along the way, the more it will help people get off the fence and support the change you want to make in your culture."

"That fits perfectly into Dr. Kotter's model … you'll see what I mean when you go through these materials. Oh, and I highly recommend getting his book, *Leading Change.* It's a great roadmap through his process," Avery said.

Kurt nodded. "We really appreciate your help and look forward to working together on this effort."

"I'm happy to help, wherever I can," the younger man said as he stood to leave. "Sorry I dropped in unannounced, but Mr. Jacobson seemed anxious for us to get acquainted."

That next Saturday, as the Air India B737-800 left the runway, its wheels retracting for the long flight to Bhopal, the three men – Kurt, Raj and Corley – sat quietly, each lost in their own thoughts. It was Kurt who finally broke the silence.

"I'm not trying to be overly dramatic, but I can't seem to get Sophie's funeral out of my mind," he began. "It was all so sudden. After the service, I met Martha's sister and she told me one day the child was normal and the next day she was struggling for every breath."

"A child's death is never easy," Corley offered, trying to comfort his friend. "It's not just the death of a child, but the death of what could have been …."

"The death of a parents' dreams for their daughter," Kurt added, lapsing into thoughtful silence.

Following the initial beverage service, Kurt began again. "Jim, ever hear of someone named Kotter?

The man seated next to him nodded his head. "John Kotter? Some of my friends call him 'the big change guru.' Why do you ask?"

"I met with Martin Avery last week. He's a new member of our management team, and one of the things Martin suggested was reading Kotter's first book, *Leading Change*. I just finished the book last night and was very impressed."

Raj joined the conversation. "I've not finished it, though what I've read makes a lot of sense."

Nodding, Kurt continued. "Kotter says the change process happens through a series of phases – eight to be exact – and these phases require a considerable length of time. He also emphasizes that you need to go through each phase."[7]

"Remind me again of what the phases are," Corley said. "It's been awhile since I read that book."

"I've summarized them on paper," said Kurt, opening his briefcase and handing both men a copy of what he had written.

[7] www.kotterinternational.com/our-principles/changesteps/changesteps

Kurt's summary read as follows:

1) **Create a sense of urgency** – Change begins when someone notices a problem area in an organization. The threat of losing ground in some way sparks these people into action, and they try to communicate that sense of urgency to others.

2) **Form a guiding coalition** – Whatever the size of the organization, the "coalition for change" should have three to five people leading the effort.

3) **Create a vision** – Picture the future showing the direction the organization needs to move in a way that's easy to communicate and appeals to everyone involved.

4) **Communicate the vision** – Estimate how much communication of the vision is needed, multiply that effort by a factor of 10 and then be seen "walking the talk."

5) **Empower others to act on the vision** – Allow people in the organization to start making changes in their areas. Find funds for the new initiative, talk about it and provide support.

6) **Create quick wins** – People won't go on the long march for change unless they see compelling evidence that their efforts are making a difference. In successfully making change, leaders plan and achieve short-term gains, which people can see and celebrate.

7) **Build on the change** – Until changes sink deeply into an organization's culture (a process that can take five to 10 years), a premature declaration of victory kills momentum, allowing tradition to regain ground.

8) **Institutionalize the change** – New behaviors may disappear unless they penetrate the organization's DNA and become

social norms and shared values. Continually show how the changes have improved the organization and make sure new-generation leaders believe in the changes, too.[8]

✦ ✦ ✦ ✦ ✦

After reading Kurt's notes, Corley looked up. "Thanks for sharing these. So let me ask you, where do you think you, as an organization, are in terms of these phases?"

"Martin and I discussed that question and he pointed out that the first two phases have been accomplished; Mr. Jacobson saw our competitor's stock price spiraling downward as a result of a chemical spill and recognized it could just as easily have happened to us."

"That's certainly a good first step," Corley agreed. "It also took a lot of courage for your CEO to recognize, admit and, more importantly, take action to ensure it doesn't happen to his company."

Kurt carried on. "Secondly, Mr. Jacobson then brought the six senior members of the management team together, including Martin, and they made the decision to devote the time, money and resources to help create a culture of environmental responsibility."

"The management team also discussed their vision of what that would look like. However, they are looking to us to come up with a plan that will appeal to everyone," Raj added.

"That's why we're headed to Bhopal," explained Kurt. "Not only are we looking for ways to approach this task but also how to communicate the need for change."

[8] www.kotterinternational.com/our-principles/changesteps/changesteps

"Kotter's approach certainly makes sense to me," Corley added, "and it's a logical way to help people embrace change."

"*Buy-In*, Dr. Kotter's newest book, is next on my reading list," responded Kurt, "and although Mr. Jacobson's support is behind us, I know there will always be people who take their time accepting the changes but must ultimately buy in if we're going to actually change the culture."

"Sounds like a good strategy," Raj agreed.

As the Air India jet made its final approach to land, the men were greeted with their first view of the Bhoj Wetland, lakes built by King Bhoj and now skirted with slender palms and other vegetation.

"Bhopal is known as one of the greenest areas of India," Raj explained as the aircraft glided smoothly onto the tarmac of Raja Bhoj Airport.

"How far are we from the city itself?" asked Kurt.

"We'll take National Highway 12 and go southeast about 8 kilometers," Raj offered. "Not a bad trip … and we're here ahead of the monsoon season."

"Glad we have Raj to keep us on track," Corley said.

After collecting their bags and settling into the minivan, Raj explained, "I've booked our rooms at the Jehan Numa Palace Hotel."

"Sounds expensive," Kurt commented.

"Oh, no. Not at all," Raj responded. "My uncle works for the hotel and our rooms will cost far less than the usual 3,645 rupees, or about $70-per-night rate."

Once registered, the three guests met at the hotel's restaurant for dinner. Enjoying shami and sheikh kebabs, the three discussed plans for the following day. "To tell you the truth, I'm not sure what I'll be looking for," Kurt confessed, "but I'll know when I see it."

"We can start with the obvious," Corley volunteered, wiping his mouth. "In order to create a culture of environmental stewardship, we first identify individual habits and corporate policies that contribute to abusing or polluting the environment. After that, we separate these from best practices … habits and policies that will improve or save the environment from harm."

"But doesn't that last part involve changing attitudes?" Raj asked.

"You're right," Kurt agreed, "and that means our next step, after identifying problems, is to develop a process that encourages individual employees to make a commitment to become stewards of the environment."

"Ah yes, that's where Kotter comes in, and that process must include a way to calculate measurable results," added Corley.

"Whew! That's going to take some doing," Kurt said finally, "but I must admit, attending Sophie's funeral made me realize that being environmentally responsible is a conscious choice each person has to make. We can argue about statistics until we're blue in the face, pardon the pun, but every day we choose to run our factories or job sites without considering the environmental impact. We're responsible – directly or indirectly – for causing more illness and premature deaths."

"Truer words have never been spoken," concurred Raj, adding sleepily, "I've charged our meal to my room, so if you don't mind, I'd like to head upstairs to get some rest for the challenge ahead."

✦ ✦ ✦ ✦ ✦

Early the next morning, a hire car was waiting for Kurt, Raj and Jim. Speaking in his native Hindi, Raj told the driver their destination. "Please take us to the site of the old chemical plant."

They were soon parked outside the skeletal remains of the chemical plant, site of the horrific disaster several decades earlier.

Guards in their khaki uniforms were playing cards on a makeshift table outside the iron gates, not bothering to abandon their game as the three men approached. Raj showed the necessary paperwork while explaining the purpose of their visit. One of the guards arose slowly from his chair to open the gates.

As the trio entered, the sounds of birds singing and cicadas chirping created a surreal contrast against the deathly silence of rusted tanks and twisted pipelines. Footpaths, now overgrown with grasses and weeds, served as a virtual feast for the goats grazing around the abandoned property.[9]

Their exploration led them into the shell of a building, its floor littered with years of accumulated debris. "This is the old control room," Corley pointed out.

As though standing among ghosts, it was not difficult for the three men to picture the panic that must have ensued in this room on that fateful December night in 1984.

"A few years back, a monitoring lab from Delhi – the Center for Science and Environment – took a water sample from a hand pump that a lot of the families in the surrounding neighborhoods still use

[9] www.youtube.com/watch?v=fdSrP7U8lLg

to this day," Raj said. "That sample contained more than 1,000 times the World Health Organization's recommended maximum of carbon tetrachloride."[10]

Corley frowned. "That is known to cause cancer."

"Exactly," Raj responded. "I fear the impact of this disaster will be felt for many more generations to come."

Toward the back of the property, Raj stopped by a rusting cylinder the size of a locomotive, which was surrounded by vines and weeds. "And this is it," he said, "Tank 610. I'm told it was originally encased in concrete, but due to the chemical reaction that night, the tank shot, spinning from its casing. That pipe," Raj continued, pointing to a piece of blackened steel, jutting 120 feet into the air, "is where 40 tons of highly poisonous methyl isocyanate[11] escaped like death into the night's air."

The three men stood silent, as if in tribute to the many fallen. "Was it the explosion that caused those gaping holes in the perimeter's brick wall?" Kurt asked.

Raj laughed. "Oh no. The missing bricks are a man-made phenomenon. You see, most of the areas around the plant were slums. People built their homes, if you can call them that, out of cardboard, wood and scraps of tin. Once the plant was abandoned, people, shall we say, 'borrowed' the bricks to construct sturdier homes."

As they left the plant, Raj led his fellow travelers down the street to view a statue of a woman pressing the head of her child against her body to protect it as she futilely tries to escape the deadly fumes. "This single memorial is so small, considering how many lives were –

[10] www.cseindia.org/content/bhopal-a-toxic-legacy
[11] http://www.dailymail.co.uk/news/article-329450/Bhopal-survivors-remember-gas-blast.html

and continue to be – affected," he said, his voice quavering.

Kurt read the plaque at the base of the concrete statue. "No More Hiroshima, No More Bhopal, We Want To Live."

The three men turned and walked somberly back to the car, sitting in silence as the car pulled away from the abandoned plant. Raj interrupted the quiet. "We'll head now to meet some of my family … and two of their friends who lived through the disaster."

"Sounds good to me," said Corley. Then he turned his attention to the traffic."You guys noticing how much exhaust is coming from the cars on the road we're passing?"

"I'm trying not to," Raj said. "India's air quality is the worst in the world … and the growing problem with pollution is caused, in part, by vehicle emissions, made worse by fuel adulteration. Plus, when you add poor fuel combustion efficiencies resulting from traffic congestion and lack of quality roads, you get a high degree of air pollution."[12, 13]

"You mean more toxic than China, Pakistan and Bangladesh?" Corley wondered aloud.

Raj grimaced. "An article printed in the *New York Times* in 2012 stated that 'untamed motorization' had wrapped New Delhi in fog or, in other words, really bad pollution, mainly due to particulates … and made worse by our growing economy.[14]

"And those particulates are especially deadly in children, right?"

Raj looked at the wedding ring on his hand and thought about the

---

[12] http://pollutedindia.weebly.com/types-of-pollution.html
[13] http://economictimes.indiatimes.com/news/economy/finance/air-pollution-costing-economy-3-75l-crore-a-year-world-bank/articleshow/21133845.cms
[14] http://esciencenews.com/sources/ny.times.science/2012/12/26/new.delhi.journal.indian.city.overwhelmed.air.pollution.new.delhi.journal

child his wife would soon deliver. "According to the statistics, respiratory problems due to polluted air contribute to 13 percent of the deaths in pediatric wards across my homeland."[15]

Kurt found himself shaking his head in frustration. "One more time … more jobs and prosperity bring more coal-fired furnaces and more automobiles on the streets."

"And air standards are not legally enforceable in India like they are in the U.S., thanks to the Clean Air Act," Raj pointed out. "But many in India's government simply brush the problem under the rug, saying the country could not enjoy the industrial growth it has if the boilers, power plants and growing number of cars were negatively impacted by laws."

"So human life doesn't count for much?" Kurt asked, already knowing the answer.

"To most people, air quality is a non-issue, especially if they have more money in their pockets and a car in their driveway," said Raj, sarcastically.

Twenty minutes later, the driver stopped the car in front of a large apartment complex.

As the three men emerged from the car, they were greeted by several members of Raj's very large family. A still-attractive older woman, dressed in a colorful traditional wrap known as a sari, threw her arms around her son, speaking first in Hindi and then English, aware of her American guests."Welcome to our home," she said.

Bowing slightly, with hands clasped, both Kurt and Corley replied with a customary greeting, "Namaste."

---

[15] http://india.blogs.nytimes.com/2012/02/01/indias-air-the-worlds-unhealthiest-study-says/

Following the group through a garden, the visitors removed their shoes before entering the home. The room had ornate tilework and high ceilings. Raj invited them to sit with him on a sofa that curved against the wall on one side of the room. Soon tea was served.

"I wanted you to meet Dr. Ahmad Patel and Dr. Sanjay Chouhan, both friends of my parents," Raj said. "Dr. Patel has been researching the Bhopal disaster, almost from day one, and Dr. Chouhan teaches at our Barkatullah University in the department of sciences."

Dr. Patel sat forward on his chair and began speaking in a hoarse voice. "One of the things Raj has told me is you're here to research environmental stewardship," he began slowly. "As we all have, I lost many friends and family over the years as a result of the disaster, and almost lost my own ability to speak."

Stopping for a moment, Patel cleared his throat. "My research has been ongoing, but perhaps the most astonishing fact I've found is, only two years before the explosion occurred, in May 1982, three engineers from West Virginia inspected the plant and found approximately 100 breaches of operational safety regulations.

"Ten of these were classified as 'major' hazards, including the potential for the release of toxic materials in the plant's MIC unit due either to equipment failure, operating or maintenance problems. Then, as production at the plant slowed, the company cut back further on staff, training and maintenance,"[16] Patel said.

"Unbelievable, but that seems to be a common response," Kurt said, putting down his teacup and shaking his head in disgust. "When sales or productivity decline, companies often think that cutbacks in personnel, safety and training are the answer."

---

[16] http://bhopal.net/rundown-to-disaster/

"You all know what happened next, so I want my friend Sanjay to share some of his experiences with you," Patel concluded, nodding to his friend.

"After that terrible night, environmental awareness and activism increased significantly in our country," Dr. Chouhan began. "The government did many things, like forming the Ministry of Environment and Forests, and they also began integrating environmental strategies into all industrial development plans."[17]

"I had been aware of that," Corley said, "It was an impressive initiative."

"Impressive, yes," Chouhan agreed, "but as you know, India's Gross National Product is growing by anywhere from 5 to 8 percent or more every year.[18] With more jobs and more people working, our government has placed much greater emphasis on continued development. I fear many of the recent regulations and policies make India's economy the priority over protecting public health and our environment."

"Happens every time," Corley said, not bothering to hide his frustration. "So, tell us more."

"Now, even though the Ministry of Environment still exists, it is in a hopeless battle to reduce industrial pollution," Patel said. "Oh, there is still talk of taking care of our environment, but our air quality has suffered because new industries coming into India rely heavily on coal-fired power plants[19] … and, more people going to work means even more automobiles on our streets, and poor enforcement of vehicle emission laws has resulted in terrible air quality."

---

[17] www.ehjournal.net/content/4/1/6

[18] http://profit.ndtv.com/news/economy/article-indias-gdp-growth-headed-towards-decade-low-of-5-per-cent-in-2012-13-cso-317539

[19] http://india.blogs.nytimes.com/2013/03/22/indias-coal-power-plants-kill-tens-of-thousands-every-year-study-says/

"Indeed, a high price for us all. A recent study found that 'exposure to coal-related pollution caused between 80,000 and 115,000 premature deaths and more than 20 million asthma attacks in 2011-12.'[20] So, are we really any better off, even as our economy grows?" Chouhan asked. "Plus another 455 coal-fired plants are in the planning stages, and that's more than four times the number we have now."

Patel shrugged. "We may have more money, but what good is it if we cannot breathe and are in poor health because no one cares about the environment?"

"With many new smaller businesses," Patel continued, "the Ministry of Environment, like your EPA, is finding it difficult to regulate waste and wastewater across the country, so our Yamuna River in New Delhi, which is a major supplier of drinking water, is now loaded with dangerously high levels of heavy metals, such as lead, cadmium, cobalt and zinc.[21]

"With the disaster we experienced in the 1980s, we could have changed the nature of India's chemical industry," the professor continued, "but instead, exposure to toxic pesticides in our agricultural areas continue and more than 3 million people die every year around the world because of the very same toxins that showered down on Bhopal almost 40 years ago.[22] We did not learn our lesson properly," he said.

After continuing the discussion for more than two hours, the three men thanked Raj's family and friends for their hospitality and the information they had shared, and then made their way back to the hotel.

---

[20] http://india.blogs.nytimes.com/2013/03/22/indias-coal-power-plants-kill-tens-of-thousands-every-year-study-says/
[21] http://www.ncbi.nlm.nih.gov/pubmed/18809251
[22] www.lenntech.com/environmental-disasters.htm

Meeting later in the hotel bar, Corley pointed out several issues that would need to be addressed as Kurt and the team began building their strategy. "Sometimes without thinking, we tolerate behaviors that really sabotage the exact goals we're trying to achieve," he offered.

"What did you see today that made you think of that?" asked Kurt.

"Well for one, the open pit where I saw the cleaning staff burning garbage," said Corley. "From what Dr. Patel told us, burning trash is the last thing India's air quality needs."

"And did you notice the barrels of food waste being loaded on to that donkey cart?"[23] Corley continued. "I saw similar barrels of waste being dumped into a canal as we were driving to your parents' apartment."

"I saw that, too, and wondered where all that food came from," Kurt added. "But it may not have all been food. Remember, everything we do creates waste of some kind."

"It's interesting, things like using a burn pit for garbage and dumping waste into the canals are accepted in our culture, it's just something people do." Contemplating his words, Raj continued. "It's the same in organizations. People have been doing things a certain way for so long, the 'company's culture' just accepts it as the norm."

"It's called an old-school mindset," Kurt interjected.

"In fact, supervisors may actually reward the very behavior we want to change," said Corley. "Take hospitals for instance, notorious for watching costs closely. Each department is rewarded for coming in under budgeted expenses. There have been many instances where medical waste washed up on a beach because someone at the hospital

[23] http://newindianexpress.com/cities/thiruvananthapuram/People%E2%80%99s-protest-against-waste-dumping-in-canal/2013/05/22/article1600947.ece

made the decision to use an unscrupulous disposal company in order to cut costs …"[24]

"And they get rewarded for not caring about the impact their decision to save money has on the environment," Kurt finished Corley's sentence.

"Okay, we're working on developing the strategies for change. What would Dr. Kotter do next?" Raj wanted to know.

Kurt thought about the question. "Next we need to find ways to communicate the message throughout the company so people will see it as worthwhile – and will buy in." His thoughts drifted to Sophie's funeral service and the little white casket. "I just hope something good can come from Sophie's death …."

[24] http://zoology.muohio.edu/oris/cunn06/cs6_23.htm

SNAPSHOT

DEFINITIONS

1. **Buy-in** – The acceptance of and commitment to a specific concept or course of action. The term is used often in the context of people agreeing to accept something and provide their support. Trying to get something done through or with others without their "buy-in" can be very difficult. Good leaders and managers know how to obtain buy-in from their stakeholders.
2. **Communication** – The activity of conveying information. Communication requires a sender, a message, and an intended recipient, although the receiver need not be present or aware of the sender's intent to communicate, which means communication can occur across vast distances in time and space.
3. **Corporate policies** – A documented set of broad guidelines, formulated after an analysis of all internal and external factors that can affect a firm's objectives, operations, and plans. Corporate policy lays down the firm's response to known and knowable situations and circumstances. It also determines the formulation and implementation of strategy, and directs and restricts the plans, decisions, and actions of the firm's officers in achievement of its objectives. Also called company policy.
4. **Empowerment** – Empowerment is the process of enabling or authorizing an individual to think, behave, take action, and control work and decision-making in autonomous ways. It is the state of feeling self-empowered to take control of one's own destiny.
5. **Environmental Performance Index** – (EPI) is a method of quantifying and numerically benchmarking the environmental

performance of a country's policies. This index was developed from the Pilot Environmental Performance Index, first published in 2002, and designed to supplement the environmental targets set forth in the U.N. Millennium Development Goals.

6. **Individual habits** – Independent of workplace guidelines or group standards, how an individual repeatedly views situations and reacts toward them. A person's routine of activities and responses from day to day.

Steps Toward Stewardship

1. For real change to occur, behavior must change.
2. To maintain a clear vision of environmental stewardship, we all must be aware of our own practices.
3. Every human activity generates waste.
4. Environmental incidents impact more than those in the immediate area, and the impact lasts longer than a few days or a few years.

Additional Activities

1. Research the Environmental Performance Index over the last two decades for any country listed. Chart the significant changes you find, identifying any trending. Then discuss reasons for those trends.
2. Using any of John Kotter's books, find a case study of a specific organization that he mentions regarding change. Then take a look at that organization's progress to date, seeking any trends that have occurred as a result of a change being introduced into that organization's culture.
3. Look up the word "empowerment." Then, find a case study for an organization that empowered its workers in any manner

and determine whether or not "empowerment" is a good tool for success.

4. Research the Bhopal disaster. Find and report any practices or situations that have been mitigated as a result of the disaster.
5. After reviewing the literature about the Bhopal disaster, determine the long-term environmental impact, to date, on the immediate environment and try to forecast the total length of the disaster's impact on India.

RESOURCES

A Force for Change, by John Kotter

Leading Change, by John Kotter

Buy-In, by John Kotter

The Heart of Change, by John Kotter and Dan Cohen

Advocacy After Bhopal, by Kim Fortun

Five Past Midnight in Bhopal, by Dominique Lapierre and Javier Moro

4 Waste/Litter/Landfills: The Battle for Survival

Returning from their trip to India, Kurt was so energized by what he had learned that he was at his desk early the following morning.

Kurt wanted to come up with ideas on how to motivate employees to embrace the vision of environmental stewardship that their CEO, Fred Jacobson, had established. At the same time, he wanted to incorporate some of the concepts and theories he had successfully used to help build the company's Culture of Safety.

"It only makes sense," Kurt said to himself, staring at the blank computer screen, "to use the same concepts – like a person's tolerance for risk, and the need for management's continual support."

"Bought your electric car yet?"

Speaking of "management support," the voice was a familiar one, and without looking up, Kurt responded. "Good morning, Mr. Kaiser … and what may I do for you this fine day?"

"Just wanted to see if you had turned green, grown a ponytail, or were hugging any trees lately," Ron Kaiser asked sarcastically.

"Not at the moment," Kurt grimaced, "but it's still early in the day."

As he turned to walk away, Kaiser almost bumped into Raj, who was walking hurriedly toward Kurt's office. "How about you, Raj? Been hugging any trees lately?" Without waiting for a reply, Kaiser laughed and continued down the long hallway toward his office.

Raj stood, watching Kaiser's retreat. Then as he stepped inside the door, he asked Kurt, "Um, did I miss something?"

"Certainly not anything worth wasting time talking about. What's up?"

"I want to show you something amazing," Raj said breathlessly, handing several sheets of paper to his boss.

Hearing the enthusiasm in his assistant's voice, Kurt stopped what he was doing and gave his full attention to the pages he had just been handed.

"In 2011, a super typhoon named Mina slammed into the Philippines," Raj began. "Thirty-five people were killed when the typhoon hit … But if that wasn't bad enough, a few days later, 20 homes were crushed by a landslide of garbage. Here, look at this photo I found on the Internet."[1]

"A landslide of garbage?" Incredulous, Kurt reached for the photo. "Wow, what a mess!"

Raj continued. "Typhoon Mina brought heavy rains, of course, which caused the city Baguio's landfill to become flooded. The flooding

[1] www.abs-cbnnews.com/nation/regions/08/29/11/typhoon-mina-leaves-17-dead-8-missing

collapsed one of the landfill's retaining walls, allowing all that garbage to come crashing down into the city.

"Now different branches of government are blaming each other for the disaster ... various laws had mandated the closing of open dump sites as far back as 2004, but residents continued to use the landfill without getting in any sort of trouble."

"Sounds familiar," Kurt commented.

"But here's how they conclude this report," Raj continued. "They say, and I quote: 'These kinds of solid waste management disasters are unfortunately not unprecedented in the Philippines and other parts of the world.'

"After seeing this report, I read about similar disasters in a shantytown in Manila, as well as southwestern China, a poor neighborhood in Brazil, and one in Indonesia.[2] I'm glad we don't have major problems with our country's landfills."

"Be careful what you assume," Kurt cautioned. "Let me tell you about a growing problem closer to home."

Raj sat down as Kurt retrieved a folder from his files. "Although not as dramatic as a landslide of garbage," he began, "according to data from the Environmental Protection Agency (EPA), every year the United States generates approximately 230 million tons of 'trash,' or about 4.6 pounds per person per day!" Kurt exclaimed. "What's more, less than one-quarter of it, or 1.5 pounds, is recycled; most of the rest is buried in landfills."[3]

"But we have plenty of landfills, right?" the younger man asked.

---

[2] http://siteresources.worldbank.org/INTUSWM/Resources/Bandung_dumpsite_disaster.pdf
[3] www.epa.gov/reg3wcmd/solidwastesummary.htm

"Like many developing countries, we are running out of room for our own garbage," his mentor continued. "Like it says here, 'Fifty percent of our landfills will be full and have to be closed within the next five to 10 years unless current facilities are expanded or new ones built … which probably won't happen because of the 'not-in-my-back-yard' mentality of most people who live in communities surrounding big cities."[4]

Raj thought for a moment. "Oh yeah, I remember NIMBY. So, what's the bottom line?"

"The bottom line, my friend, is that we, as a nation – and as a planet, for that matter – need to become more proactive," Kurt replied.

"Proactive?" Raj seemed puzzled. "So, how can we be proactive … about garbage?"

"A while ago, I saw a newspaper article reporting that one of the largest waste management companies in the U.S. will be opening a pilot plant that will convert used plastic into 75,000 barrels of oil per year. And, while some say the main environmental threat from biodegradable waste is the production of methane,[5] this same company also captures the methane gas generated from decomposing garbage at more than 100 landfills. This strategy alone generated enough electrical power in 2011 to power 1.17 million homes,"[6] Kurt explained.

Sounding hopeful, Raj asked "So it sounds like this waste management company has found the answer to a couple of problems with its latest initiative, right?"

"You would think so, but not exactly," Kurt replied. "Unfortunately,

---

[4] http://postcom.org/eco/facts.about.landfills.htm
[5] http://ec.europa.eu/environment/waste/compost/index.htm
[6] *The Houston Chronicle*, Dec. 30, 2012

companies like this don't always get paid enough to dispose of the waste to make these alternative energy sources economically viable."

"Well, what's it going to take for people around the world to wake up and realize we have a real problem when it comes to landfills?" Raj wondered aloud.

"Landfills are not our only problem when it comes to garbage," Kurt warned. "Ever hear of the floating landfills? They were first found in the Pacific but have more recently turned up in the Atlantic Ocean,"[7] he began.

"One of these trash piles is called 'the Great Pacific Garbage Patch,' and some say it's the largest landfill on Earth!" Kurt continued, leafing through a file. "Ah, here it is … and I quote, 'It is the poster child for a worldwide problem: plastic and other debris that begins in human hands ends up in the ocean, often inside animals' stomachs or around their necks. One sea turtle found dead in Hawaii was said to have had more than 1,000 pieces of plastic in its intestines[8] while others have been found dead after swallowing entire plastic bags.'"[9]

Raj looked disgusted. "So, our trash on land has begun polluting our oceans. I wonder what that decaying plastic does to other sea life?"

"Exactly!" Kurt said, "So we have chemical contamination as well as tons of garbage in the oceans … and, here's an interesting side note: In 1992, a shipping container transporting 28,000 rubber ducks fell off a freighter and was lost at sea. Since that incident, those little yellow rubber duckies have continued to wash ashore and many have been reported. These reports have given scientists more information about the ocean's gyres and the Pacific garbage patch.[10]

---

[7] www.mnn.com
[8] www.mnn.com
[9] http://www.mnn.com/earth-matters/animals/stories/turtle-found-that-pooped-plastic-for-a-month-0
[10] http://ecopreservationsociety.org/site/index.php/the-news/conservation-costa-rica/318-what-can-28000-rubber-duckies-lost-at-sea-teach-us-about-our-oceans

"But, back to the garbage problem. I want to share one more interesting bit of information I found:

"'The Great Pacific Garbage Patch has grown 100-fold since the 1970s and is now estimated to be about the size of Texas, with about 80 percent – or 5.5 million tons of debris[11] – coming from land. United Nations' estimates say free-floating fishing nets make up another 10 percent of all marine litter, or about 705,000 tons.[12] The rest comes from recreational boaters, offshore oil rigs and large cargo ships, which amazingly drop about 10,000 steel shipping containers into the sea each year ... full of who-knows-what dangerous chemicals," Kurt said.

"I don't understand why that's happening ... and I'd like to know more," said Raj. "Wonder if Dr. Corley can shed any light on this problem?"

"We can find out," Kurt said, looking at his calendar.

"Just let me know when," Raj said, "because, if you'll pardon the pun, when it comes to environmental awareness, I feel like a fish out of water."

✦ ✦ ✦ ✦ ✦

Jim Corley was waiting on his front porch when Kurt and Raj drove up the driveway. "Come in," he said. "I'll get coffee while you make yourselves comfortable in the study."

Almost as soon as the guests seated themselves on the brown leather sofa, Corley returned, carrying a tray laden with three mugs of coffee and a plate of cookies. "Glad you both could make it this morning," he said. "So, what's on your agenda?"

---

[11] www.telegraph.co.uk/earth/environment/9253665/Great-Pacific-Garbage-Patch-has-increased-100-fold-since-the-1970s.html

[12] http://www.mnn.com/earth-matters/wilderness-resources/photos/americas-10-worst-man-made-environmental-disasters/pacific

"We've been discussing the Great Pacific Garbage Patch," Kurt began. "Anyone come up with ideas about how to clean it up?"

The older man winced and sighed. "To answer your question, the Scripps Institute estimated the cost of cleaning up the garbage patch would bankrupt any country.[13] But before we discuss 'the patch' further, let's first look at how it actually happened," said Corley. "Any guesses?"

His guests sat quietly.

"Well, the short answer is Humans + Ocean Currents = Trash Vortex."[14] Corley glanced up to see Kurt and Raj already taking notes as he spoke.

"It is estimated there are actually five vortexes of garbage in our oceans today. A fellow by the name of Stiv Wilson of the 5 Gyres Project has released a preliminary estimate, saying there are 315 billion pounds of debris in the ocean right now.[15]

"So, here we are, with all this garbage, heading toward the ocean … and a person might say, 'Well, the ocean's so big ….'"

"But we have to think about what this garbage is doing to sea life, don't we?" asked Raj.

"Let's begin with little fish on the lower end of the ocean's food chain that consume tiny bits of plastic, mistaking these bits for food. These little fish, in turn, are eaten by bigger fish and these end up on our plates for dinner … so we're now quite literally eating our own plastic garbage."[16]

"Well, there goes my appetite for seafood," Kurt declared.

---

[13] http://news.nationalgeographic.com/news/2009/07/090731-ocean-trash-pacific.html
[14] www.howstuffworks.com/environmental/conservation/issues/great-pacific-garbage-patch-explained.htm
[15] www.howstuffworks.com/environmental/conservation/issues/great-pacific-garbage-patch-explained.htm
[16] www.nrdc.org/oceans/plastic-ocean/

"So, the next question is, 'What can be done?'" Corley continued, "and the answer is a real cleanup would be astronomically expensive, both in terms of dollars and equipment."

"Well, if a cleanup isn't possible, how can we keep the problem from getting any worse?" Kurt wondered aloud.

Corley stood and walked to a file cabinet and thumbed through some papers. "Ah, here it is," he said, opening a file. "When we want to clean up the environment, whether it's in our water, on land, or the air we breathe, we – and I mean individuals as well as companies – need to decide to live life in a way that's both environmentally friendly and sustainable for future generations."

"There's that word again – sustainable," Raj spoke up.

Corley smiled. "And, in case you forgot, it means maintaining a balance between our consumption of natural resources and ensuring the availability of these for future generations, which is one of the six simple principles that people, as well as companies, need to adopt if we are going to reduce environmental damage. Here, I'll show you the principles:

1. Reduce pollution.
2. Conserve resources.
3. Conserve energy.
4. Reduce consumption and waste.
5. Protect the earth's ecological balance.
6. Design products with "lifecycle" in mind.

"Each of these principles are designed to protect the environment from harm," the older man said, "but they also help sustain living conditions needed by us humans."

"So, this is about more than recycling paper," Kurt added.

"Absolutely. It's much, much more," Corley nodded. "Let me give you an example of a company designing products with 'lifecycle' in mind:

"Ford Motor Company's use of splash shields, engine covers and other components made from recycled plastics has prevented an estimated 25 million to 30 million pounds of plastic from going into landfills, according to company statistics,"[17] he said.

"As another example, the 2010 Ford Taurus was the 11th Ford vehicle to have seat cushions, seatbacks, and headrests made from soy- and biomass-based foam … and these also were included in the Ford Mustang and eight other of their vehicles … which is why Ford has made the claim that their cars are 85 percent recyclable.[18]

"Ford also has used seat fabrics made from recycled yarn in their Escape and Escape Hybrid. The 2010 Ford Flex is outfitted with storage bins constructed from wheat straw-reinforced plastic. Ford's goal is to eventually make cars where none of the plastic components are made from petroleum but from materials that are completely compostable," he said.

"But that's just one company," Kurt observed.

"I'm just getting started, my friend," Corley responded.

"Other companies are:

- "Creating a culture of environmental stewardship that not only helps make the world a better place; businesses also discover they're actually saving money. Not to mention increasing goodwill among

[17] http://news.cnet.com/8301-11128_3-20003169-54.html
[18] http://news.cnet.com/8301-11128_3-20003169-54.html

the community and appealing to customers who want to do business with 'green' companies.

✦ "Using virtual employees – particularly in administrative and technology operations – and creating alternative work environments for employees who are able to work from home, otherwise known as telecommuting.

"With 40 percent of their employees telecommuting, International Business Machines believes it has saved close to $2.9 billion in reduced space needs since 1995 – and this doesn't include energy cost savings."[19]

"That's impressive," Kurt said.

"And this figure doesn't include the fuel savings each telecommuter realizes, which – according to a 2011 survey – found each employee who telecommutes only twice monthly saves around 46 gallons of gasoline per year,"[20] the older man added.

✦ "Going paperless – by using electronic ordering, electronic invoicing, electronic records, proposals and files, as well as using email rather than sending memos.

"Don't most firms do this automatically these days?" asked Raj.

"No, not automatically," Corley responded, "but they should if, for no other reason, they want to save money."

"So, how much can be saved?"

"Let's take a small company with eight employees. Majestic Invites, an e-commerce invitation design company in the U.S., estimates they

[19] www.smartplanet.com/blog/transportation/study-telecommuting-can-save-american-households-17-billion-per-year/221
[20] www.epa.gov/region9/waste/solid/reduce.html

save about $50,000 annually by going paperless," Corley said, "but if you want to talk about larger organizations, like a hospital with 350 employees, for example, they can save $1 million annually simply by switching to electronic medical records.[21]

"The positive side of going paperless," Corley continued, "is that most organizations making the switch from paper to paperless report being able to do more with less, and that includes improved customer service, as well as a much-improved culture where employees work together more easily and, in some cases, actually become more engaged due to these streamlined processes."[22]

"If I could interrupt you for a minute, I'd like to point something out," Kurt asked.

Corley smiled, "Please do. It seems like I've been doing all of the talking this morning."

"You brought up an important point about people being able to see the difference their behavior is making," Kurt began. "As John Kotter's sixth step tells us, a company has to 'first take baby steps and create short-term wins that people can see.'"

"Remember, we also found that to be the case when the company's safety culture started to improve," Raj said. "Our people had to start believing that their change in behavior resulted in a safer work environment."

"A change that management then had to celebrate, especially in the beginning, even if it was just a small success," Kurt added.

"And, let's not forget that our company is now saving millions of dollars

---

[21] www.cisco.com/web/solutions/smb/need_to/the_path_to_paperless.html
[22] www.inc.com/guides/2010/06/switch-to-paperless-office.html

annually as a result of our safety culture," Raj reminded the group. "This certainly helps ensure management's continued buy-in …."

"Which, as we know, is the foundation of a company's culture, whether we're talking about safety or environmental stewardship," Kurt said, finishing Corley's sentence.

"But, you'd be surprised how slow some companies and organizations have been to adopt the electronic-rather-than-paperless environment, or any of the environmental principles we've talked about so far," Corley said and sighed.

Kurt agreed. "Don't remind me. As a champion for corporate cultural change, I now know the only thing slower than creating changes in behavior may be waiting for rain in the Sahara Desert."

Corley chuckled. "Sometimes it feels like the rain may come sooner."

"Well hopefully it won't be acid rain," Raj joked.

"You never know," the older man retorted. "Where was I? Oh yes. Corporate benefits from environmental stewardship. Let's begin with:

"Reducing energy usage. I've noticed many new buildings being constructed around the country are 'green' buildings."[23]

"Which means?" Kurt asked.

"These newer buildings have been designed to conserve all sorts of resources – like situating the building to take advantage of natural lighting, which reduces their electricity and some heating or air-conditioning costs," Corley continued. "Every piece of equipment is

[23] http://officeinsight.org/economic-benefits-of-green-buildings-highlighted/

Energy Star certified[24] for efficient use of power, from computers to refrigeration in labs and from heating and cooling to outdoor lighting in private homes and public buildings.

"The new environmentally friendly – in other words 'green' – buildings I've visited so far also conserve water by installing things like rainwater collection systems, low-flush toilets, and reduced-volume sinks. They also put up signs to remind people of the importance of conservation.

"The companies that have, shall I say 'turned green' also rely on ecofriendly materials in their shipping activities, and many of their company-owned vehicles are either hybrids or electric," Corley concluded.

"So, these companies are truly serious about doing their bit to sustain ecological balance on the planet?" Kurt asked as he scribbled notes.

"If you want to see just how committed these folks are to environmental stewardship, you need to visit their worksites," Corley said. "Of course, their numbers are small – not enough companies want to take the time to clean up their environmental messes – but every change always begins with one or two leaders."

"You guys have time to take a quick fieldtrip?" asked Corley.

"Only if you will let us buy lunch while we are out," Kurt joked.

"Great, I know a good 'seafood' restaurant," Corley suggested, quickly turning his back before Kurt could see the wide grin on his face.

Looking absently at his shoe, Raj broke the silence as the three men rode in Corley's diesel-run pickup truck. "I know this is no big deal,

---

[24] www.energystar.gov/

but at my apartment I noticed there are two kinds of pet owners – the ones who are very careful to clean up after their dogs and those who allow their animals to leave droppings everywhere. Just the other night, I stepped in some, and I have to tell you, if anybody had been walking their dog at the time, I would have given them bloody hell."

"Couldn't you have waited until after lunch to share this observation with us?" chided Kurt. "I'm just joking. It's the same thing in my neighborhood, so I really appreciate the people who carry plastic bags with them to pick it up."

"Yeah, that's something I thought, too … at first," Raj responded. "But, that's not as helpful as it sounds. You're sitting here, praising people for using plastic to clean up after their dogs when that's the same plastic that some studies have shown will take 500-1,000 years to biodegrade in our landfills."[25]

"Curious?" Corley asked. "So are there other options out there?"

"Actually, there are," Raj confirmed, slightly embarrassed that he had become an expert on dog poop. "There are biodegradable, compostable, even flushable bags. A good biodegradable bag will even dissolve in the airless environment of a landfill, which occurs when the waste is compacted."

"Wow, we might just have to add the title of 'Super Duper Pooper Scooper' to your business card," Kurt joked, further adding to Raj's already red face.

After driving for several miles, the three men arrived at one of the city's landfills.

[25] www.petside.com/article/dog-poop-cleanup-rethinking-plastic-bags

Standing at the top of a grassy knoll, nearly 100 feet high, Corley pointed out several landmarks. "This knoll, for example, is actually a stack of trash that's been covered with a layer of soil and then planted," he explained. "That section over there is ready for the same treatment. So, while it'll look like meadowland, the land really isn't going to be good for much. The landfill itself is quickly reaching capacity."

"So, what's the alternative?" Kurt asked.

"Well ... a world population committed to reduce, reuse, recycle and restore would be a good starting point," said the older man.

"But that'll take years," Raj sighed. "What's our next best alternative?"

"We could start by finding new ways to handle garbage," Corley said, "and, believe me, there have been some interesting twists and turns along the way."

"What do you mean?" asked Kurt.

"Well, for example, in 1987 the Mobro Barge left Islip, N.Y., loaded with 3,100 tons of trash," Corley began. "It was originally destined for Morehead City, N.C., as part of a solid-waste-to-methane pilot project. However, the citizens of Morehead City said, "NIMBY" and the city managers turned the garbage-laden barge away.[26]

"Looking for another place to dump its smelly cargo, the barge continued down the east coast of North America but found no takers," he continued. "The barge turned toward Mexico, however, the Mexican Navy met the barge and denied entrance to their waters. It then moved on to the Caribbean and to Belize, where it was again turned away before it headed back to New York City."

---

[26] www.nytimes.com/1987/07/11/nyregion/trash-barge-to-end-trip-in-brooklyn.html

"How long did this infamous voyage take … and how much did it cost?" Kurt asked.

"By the time the trash reached New York City, was off-loaded, incinerated in Brooklyn and the resulting 400 tons of ash was trucked to Islip and buried – which as you may remember was where it started in the first place – the trip took 12 days and cost well over $1 million," Corley explained.

Raj was shaking his head. "Unbelievable."

"But this story has a silver lining," Corley quickly countered. "It became a national symbol of North America's lack of sound solid-waste disposal strategies. You see, between 1982 and 1987, more than 3,000 landfills across the U.S. closed[27] … and the Mobro Barge's seemingly endless voyage caught the attention of the world's media, who in turn shone their bright lights on the problem: society's overconsumption, lack of landfill space and alternatives to solid waste disposal."

"You said that was back in 1987?" Kurt asked. "Is that when the country's larger cities began offering recycling services?"

"Actually, by 1976, quite a few states had established a return deposit program for certain items, like soft-drink bottles, and a number of cities had curbside recycling programs to lessen the impact of garbage on landfills.[28] The recyclables are then separated into metal, glass, rubber and paper," Corley explained, "which are then turned into any number of products.

"But here is something else to think about," the older man continued. "According to the Pew Research Center, 85 percent of Americans own mobile phones."[29]

---

[27] www.bos.frb.org/economic/nerr/rr2002/q1/waste.htm
[28] www.acedisposal.com/history/history_garbage.aspx
[29] http://pewinternet.org/Commentary/2012/February/Pew-Internet-Mobile.aspx

Quickly doing the math in his head, Raj responded, "That's about 255 million phones."

"That's right," Corley confirmed. "The average lifespan of a mobile phone is 18 months and, according to the Environmental Protection Agency, only 25 percent of those 255 million phones are recycled, which is the lowest rate among recyclable products."

"If you think about all of the computers and tablets that are out there, too, it sounds like we need to keep 'e-waste' in mind as well," Kurt commented.

The men stood, looking out over the vast landfill for several minutes before Corley said, "Okay, fellows. Let's go grab that bite to eat before we head back to the house."

"Sounds good. I'm looking forward to a big 'Hamburger', with a capital 'H,'" Kurt joked.

Later on, back in his office, Jim Corley showed Kurt and Raj a list of statistics he had collected about the current picture of garbage recycling in America. "These are based on numbers from the Environmental Protection Agency collected in 2009,"[30] he added as he handed his two guests copies:

- ✦ **251 million** – tons of trash in the United States.
- ✦ **82 million** – tons of materials recycled in the United States.
- ✦ **53.4** – percent of all paper products recycled in the United States.
- ✦ **32.5** – percent of total waste that is recycled in the United States, versus 60 percent in Austria, the leading recycler in the European Union.

[30] www.epa.gov/osw/nonhaz/municipal/msw99.htm

- **8,875** – number of curbside recycling programs in the United States in 2003.
- **8,660** – number of curbside recycling programs in the United States in 2006.
- **6** – weeks it takes to manufacture, fill, sell, recycle and re-manufacture an aluminum beverage container.

Kurt and Raj sat for a moment, trying to absorb the statistics they had been given. "We're talking about changing the behavior of an entire country," Kurt said, looking at the list, "but recycling programs are actually going down in numbers – probably because of costs – and we're trying to change behaviors?"

"That may be the case in the U.S. but definitely not in other countries around the globe, particularly the island countries or those, such as Germany, that are landlocked," Corley explained.

"We were just talking about that before we came over," Raj said. "Please tell us what you know."

"In landlocked countries, the people have made 'green' not only a government initiative but also have formed a 'green party' and elected representatives who uphold environmental stewardship," Corley said. "Their fear of running out of space – due to expanding landfills, as an example – has also made recycling, reuse and overall efforts to decrease waste somewhat emotional, as well."[31]

"What about island countries?"

"If you mean countries like Japan, their efforts have long outpaced the U.S. for keeping landfill waste to a minimum," Corley continued.

[31] http://wps.prenhall.com/wps/media/objects/2513/2574258/pdfs/E11.1.pdf

"Recycling rates in Japan are much higher than those of the United States. Only something like 16 percent of waste in Japan is sent to landfills compared to about 60 percent to 70 percent in the United States,[32] but let's get back to changing behaviors. Kurt, you sound like you don't think this may be possible."

Kurt shook his head. "No, no. I don't want to give you that impression. It just seems like people not bothering to take time to reduce, reuse, recycle and restore is … dare I say it … such a 'waste' …."

[32] www.econedlink.org/lessons/index.php?lid=218&type=student

SNAPSHOT

DEFINITIONS

1. **Biomass** – Biological material derived from living or recently living organisms. In the context of biomass for energy, this is often used to mean plant-based material, but biomass can equally apply to both animal- and vegetable-derived material.
2. **Curbside recycling** – A service provided to households – typically in urban and suburban areas – of removing household waste, separating paper, plastic, glass, cardboard, metals, green waste and kitchen waste and reusing "waste" to manufacture new goods.
3. **E-waste** – Discarded electrical or electronic devices. Some are recycled while others are processed separately from other landfill waste, as e-waste may contain harmful elements, such as lead, cadmium and others.
4. **Landfill** – Also known as a dump, rubbish dump or dumping ground, a landfill is a site for the disposal of waste materials by burial and is the oldest form of waste treatment.
5. **Methane gas (CH4)** – The second most prevalent greenhouse gas emitted in the United States from human activities. In 2011, CH4 accounted for about 9 percent of all U.S. greenhouse gas emissions from human activities. Methane gas, also called "swamp gas," is emitted by natural sources such as wetlands and decaying vegetation as well as human activities, including industry, agriculture, and waste management activities.
6. **Typhoon** – Tropical cyclones in the western Pacific are called typhoons; those in the Atlantic and eastern Pacific Ocean are called hurricanes. It's the longitude that matters.

7. **Waste management** – The collection, transport, processing or disposal, managing and monitoring of waste materials produced by human activity.

Steps Toward Stewardship

1. The vision for change, as well as the result of that change, must be made "real" to others through stories and examples.
2. Awareness of the long-term results of environmentally abusive behaviors is essential to inspire others to change behaviors.
3. When our behaviors impact us and those we care about, we are more apt to want to learn how to make positive changes.
4. The importance of reduce, reuse, recycle and restore cannot be overstated.
5. Be aware: All waste comes from human activities. It is up to us to control this fact of life.

Additional Activities

1. Explore the recycling initiatives in your hometown. Report "the good, the bad and the ugly" data about local landfills, capacities and efforts to decrease landfill waste. If available, report the costs and/or savings of these recycling programs.
2. Pick any country and study their efforts in environmental stewardship. Then, compare these initiatives to those in our country.
3. What is the importance (and the global advantage) of the 5 Gyre Project?
4. Over the span of one weekend (Friday, Saturday, Sunday), try to keep your personal waste (food, food containers, glass and plastic bottles, etc.) to less than a pound. Bring this to the

group. After completing this initiative, write down what you did to manage your waste.

5. Divide into groups. Devise a presentation to the officials at Acme Tomato Cannery, showing how they can add to their bottom line with environmental stewardship initiatives. Give the presentation to all groups.

Water Conservation/ Management: Looking for Environmental Conversation Opportunities

After a weekend of catching up with family and some long-neglected household chores, Kurt was back at his office bright and early Monday morning, piecing together what he was learning and where his company needed to begin their new culture of environmental stewardship.

Kurt realized his life was changing as he was becoming more aware of the environment and the ongoing abuse of precious resources. No longer was his family buying bottled water. Instead, they were using filters on the taps of their kitchen and bathroom sinks. His wife, Jessica, attended a class on how to harvest rainwater and was now working on redesigning their yard in order to eliminate the need for watering. Kurt smiled to himself as he thought about how he now even worked side by side with his mother-in-law, Janet, at her recycling club.

His office environment had begun evolving, too. He was now making a point of re-using manila file folders, saving used paper for recycling and, after a meeting with the building's owner and making a strong case for cost savings, energy-efficient lighting was being installed, floor by floor, and water-efficient fixtures were now used to replace those that stopped working. With these last two changes, the owner was also taking advantage of the city's rebate programs that offered discounts and cash back on environmentally friendly improvements.

He had just finished reading over his notes from his last visit with Jim Corley when Fred Jacobson walked into his office. As the older man sat down across from his desk, Kurt noticed Fred was drinking his coffee from a ceramic cup. Kurt held up his own mug. "I'm glad to see, as the CEO of the company, you're demonstrating environmental stewardship by eliminating the use of Styrofoam cups."

Jacobson chuckled. "Knowledge is power, right?"

"I think the late President Harry Truman got it right when he said, 'It's what you learn after you know it all that counts,'" Kurt responded.

Jacobson chuckled again and nodded. "I like that. Just about says it all." He cleared his throat before he continued. "Kurt, I'm working on a special project and would like your opinion. It's called 'SOPHIE Says.'"

Kurt swallowed hard at the mention of the little girl's name they had only recently lost. "How are Martha and her husband holding up since the funeral?" Kurt asked somberly.

"They are doing as well as one might expect," responded Jacobson. "My wife, Mary, and I had them over at the house for dinner a couple of weeks ago. It was a few days later that Mary came up with the idea for SOPHIE Says."

"You've piqued my interest. Can you tell me more about it?" Kurt said, leaning forward.

"Well, it's still in the early stages so I'd appreciate it if you would keep it between you and me at this point," requested the CEO.

"Absolutely, I won't say a word to anyone."

"During our dinner, Martha told us how Sophie used to love playing the game Simon Says with her father," Jacobson began. "As you can imagine, it soon became Sophie Says. They would play every morning during breakfast, and it was the last thing they would do together before Sophie went to bed at night."

Kurt pictured his own daughter at that age. "I can remember playing Simon Says with Shannon."

"Her father, David, said he still wakes up in the morning and expects to hear his daughter squeal with delight, 'Sophie Says, Daddy … Sophie Says.'"

There was a moment of silence, two fathers lost in their own thoughts of years gone by.

Jacobson cleared his throat before continuing. "As I was saying, a few days after our dinner with Martha and her husband, my wife asked what I thought about the idea of starting a fund called Sophie Says in honor of little Sophie. "Here's the best part though … and Mary came up with this too: SOPHIE stands for **S**ave **O**ur **P**lanet **H**elp **I**ncrease **E**nvironmentalism."

"What a great idea!" Kurt exclaimed.

"My feeling exactly, and I am really proud of Mary for coming up with the idea," Jacobson continued, failing to hide his excitement. "So, we've established the Sophie Says foundation … and anyone interested can go on the Internet to www.sophiesays.org and make a donation. Then, 100 percent of the profits will go toward raising environmental awareness."

"You can certainly count on Jessica and me to donate. And I know Raj and most of our employees will do so as well. So just let me know when I can start spreading the word," Kurt replied enthusiastically.

"Thanks, Kurt. I know it will never take away the pain of losing their daughter," the CEO paused and swallowed hard again, "but I hope by honoring her through Sophie Says – while helping the environment – this huge loss will be just a little more bearable." Jacobson looked at his watch. "I have a meeting to get to in five minutes, but I appreciate your input."

✦ ✦ ✦ ✦ ✦

Standing in the company's break room later that day, Kurt noticed a guy washing out his coffee cup. What caught Kurt's attention was that the younger man did not turn off the water as he stood there drying the cup before placing it up on the shelf … even going so far as wiping the countertop, all the while water was pouring down the drain.

Thinking the young man to be a summer intern, Kurt decided this was a good time to see if the "Safety 24/7 Conversation," which was being used across the company to help prevent incidents, could be used to raise environmental awareness.

"Hi there, my name's Kurt Bradshaw. Can I speak with you for a moment?".

"Sure, what can I do for you?" the younger man responded cordially.

"I appreciate you keeping this area clean by wiping down the countertop after washing your cup. Not every employee bothers to cleanup after themselves," Kurt paused. "There was something, however, that caused me some concern as I was watching you. Do you know what that might be?"

After thinking for a moment, the man replied "Um, I'm really not sure … maybe I didn't wash out the cup well enough or maybe I put it back in the wrong place?"

Kurt smiled. "No, I'm sure you did all of that just fine. But once you were done washing the cup, was it necessary to keep the water running while you wiped down the counter?"

"I really did not give it much thought, but I guess it wasn't," the younger man admitted.

Moving to the next step of what had now become a "24/7 Environmental Conversation," Kurt asked, "How bad would it be if you turned on your faucet one day and no water came out … and believe me, this has happened in several states already?"[1, 2]

"Wow! That would be terrible," came the man's response.

"Then let me ask you, what would be the worst thing about it?" Kurt continued.

"I guess there would be a lot, but two I can think of right away because they happened this morning when I went into the kitchen for breakfast. There was a pan boiling on the stove that had several baby bottle nipples in it that my wife was sterilizing. Secondly, we have a humidifier going in our 5-month-old's room to help with his congestion," the new father explained.

"So, can I get you to commit to turning off the water when you're doing something like wiping down the counter?" Kurt asked hopefully.

---

[1] www.guardian.co.uk/environment/2013/may/24/global-majority-water-shortages-two-generations
[2] http://oklahomawatch.org/2013/03/22/as-water-dwindles-will-oklahomans-conserve/

"Sure, no problem," agreed the younger man. "You know, now that I'm thinking about it, I realize how much water I waste, while I'm shaving or brushing my teeth, leaving the water on the entire time."[3]

"If the average person in the U.S. spends 45 seconds brushing their teeth and keeping the water running as they do so, they'll waste a little more than 1,800 gallons of water every year.[4]" Kurt said.

"That's incredible. By the way, my name's Neal Jacobson III," offered the younger man.

Kurt smiled. "Jacobson? That name sounds familiar. Any relation to our CEO?"

"Uh, yes. He's my uncle," Neal replied. "I just started working here. In fact, I was a little nervous when you approached me and said I caused you 'some concern.' Anyway, I really appreciate how you took the time to help me realize how much water I was wasting."

"You're welcome," responded Kurt. "But actually, I have to thank you for helping me with a project I'm working on. You see, I just proved the 'Safety 24/7 Conversation' we use throughout the company to help people avoid safety-related incidents can also be used to help raise environmental awareness."

"I get it," exclaimed Neal. "It's hard for people to accept feedback, but specific feedback provided in a positive manner, like you just did, is effective, whether it is safety- or environmentally related."

"You really do 'get it,'" Kurt exclaimed, "and, if you'd be interested, I could use another member on my project team. I'm going to speak with your uncle, but why don't you plan on coming to my office at 7 a.m. tomorrow?"

[3] www.philau.edu/collegestudies/Documents/Audrey%20Kender.pdf
[4] http://www.you-can-go-green.com/2009/07/how-much-water-do-we-waste-brushing-our.html

"Okay. Yes, I would be interested," said the younger Jacobson. "But, if you don't mind me saying, you sure work fast …."

Looking out the window at the brown haze, Kurt grimaced. "Once you get involved in this project, you soon realize we might not be working fast enough."

✦ ✦ ✦ ✦ ✦

By this time, the workroom that separated Kurt's office from Raj's was piled with books and other materials about environmental stewardship. As he looked over the stacks of data waiting to be researched, Kurt shook his head, remembering Jim Corley's comment about "having barely scratched the surface."

Kurt was about to toss the morning paper to the side. That is, until he saw the headline emblazoned across the top of the front page: "Hydro-diplomacy needed to avert Arab water wars."[5] After quickly scanning the article, Kurt dialed Jim Corley's number.

"Good morning, Kurt," he answered. "What's going on?"

"Seen this morning's paper, Jim?"

"You're calling about the water wars story," Corley surmised.

"Well, I have heard about water shortages before," Kurt admitted, "but I guess I didn't think it had become that bad."

"Trying to soothe your guilty conscience," Corley chuckled. "I'd say the first moderate shortage began at the beginning of the 19th century, but it took about 100 more years to make an impact. That's when somewhere around two percent of the world's population experienced the first ongoing water shortage."

[5] www.reuters.com/article/2011/03/20/us-climate-water-idUSTRE72J2W620110320

"So, it's a real possibility, especially in the Middle East and North Africa?" Kurt questioned. "I don't remember reading that Armageddon was going to be all about water."

Corley chuckled again. "No, me neither, but by the 1960s, the water shortage had gained momentum and by 2005, it had increased from 9 percent of the population, or roughly 280 million people, to 35 percent, or 2.3 billion people. But just in case you're thinking climate change is the sole reason, let me surprise you: Population increase has been four times more significant in the rise of the global water shortage."[6]

"So, why hasn't the press made more noise about it?" Kurt wondered aloud.

"You know how politicians are ..." replied Corley. "They don't want the media to talk about water shortages when their town, or country for that matter, relies on tourism for a large part of the economy."

"Politicians might not want to scare away tourists, but rather than bury their heads in the sand, I can remember hotels began placing signs in the bathrooms years ago asking guests to conserve water," Kurt recalled.

"I bet you have now seen hotels going even further in their efforts to conserve water, asking guests if they really need their bed linens and towels washed every day," Corley mentioned. "Not only does it help the environment but it also saves the hotel money. For example, I just read that a hotel with 250 rooms at 80 percent occupancy could save up to $66,000 and 220,000 gallons of water per year.[7] But, let's talk about this further when we meet on Friday."

"Sounds good. I'd also like to bring along my new research intern, Neal Jacobson ... Fred Jacobson's nephew."

---

[6] Matti Kummu, Aalto University, Finland @ environmentalresearchweb.org.
[7] http://apus-sustainability.com/how-much-water-is-saved-by-reusing-hotel-towels-and-linens/

Corley chuckled. "Sounds to me like you're putting together a pretty high-profile team!"

"I'm looking for speed and this young man is a quick study," Kurt said before ending the conversation with his mentor.

✦ ✦ ✦ ✦ ✦

The next Friday found Kurt and Neal Jacobson meeting in Jim's study where the two older men were enjoying coffee.

"So, let's talk about water," Kurt began.

Corley smiled. "Okay, which of the three parts?"

Kurt looked puzzled. "You mean like the 'H', the '2' or the 'O'?" he asked, giving the commonly accepted scientific chemical composition for water, H_2O.

Corley smiled.

"Not exactly … if we talk about water, we divide the conversation into three parts …" the older man explained. "First, there's 'conservation.' Our global water supply is disappearing at an alarming rate, now more than ever. So, there's the effort to conserve our current resources. Secondly, there's the effort to deliver clean water. Although we don't see it on this continent as much, the World Health Organization reported in 2008 that more than 3.4 million people die each year because of polluted water, sanitation and hygiene-related causes. Close to 99 percent of these deaths occur in the developing world."[8]

Neal's eyes widened as he heard the statistics.

[8] World Health Organization (WHO). (2008). Safer Water, Better Health: Costs, benefits, and sustainability of interventions to protect and promote health; Updated Table 1

"But here's something else we should keep in mind," Corley added. "The lack of access to clean water and sanitation kills children at a rate equivalent to a jumbo jet crashing every four hours.[9]

"Unbelievable," the younger man gasped.

Kurt was pleased to hear that his young colleague was getting the point. "And I just read recently that a person taking a five-minute shower uses more water than a person living in the slums of a developing country has access to for an entire day.[10]

Neal put down his notebook. "So water shortages are primarily happening outside the U.S.?"

"Not exactly" Corley smiled, "In 2012, a record-breaking drought occurred. By December of that year, more than 62 percent of the U.S. was experiencing 'moderate to exceptional' drought, which extended into 2013.[11]

"That year-long drought impacted water systems throughout the country, and if this lack of rain continues, it could drastically affect areas like the Mississippi River," he continued. "If the water levels continue to drop there, barge traffic and billions of dollars worth of agricultural, fuel and chemical products could be severely impacted."

Corley paused. "As usual, I've strayed a bit from our topic (water shortages), but I want you to see the big picture."

Neal nodded. "I'm beginning to, but I'm not too sure I like the picture you're painting."

---

[9] Estimated with data from Diarrhea: Why children are still dying and what can be done. UNICEF, WHO 2009

[10] United Nations Development Programme (UNDP). (2006). Human Development Report 2006, "Beyond Scarcity: Power, Poverty and the Global Water Crisis"

[11] New York Times, Feb. 17, 2013. http://topics.nytimes.com/top/news/science/topics/drought/index.html http://www.nytimes.com/2012/08/24/us/midwest-water-wells-drying

"Like it or not, Jim is giving us the facts, and part of that scenario is hitting pretty close to home. Did you know that Texas cities use more than 1.3 trillion gallons of water each year? Some of my family live in West Texas," Kurt explained. "The lake they depend on is almost dry, so they've been rationing water for more than a year. Many families are having water trucked in at a cost of $1,000 a month, just to water their livestock and then to shower, brush their teeth and cook."[12]

"Sounds really inconvenient, not to mention incredibly expensive," the intern responded.

"Oh, wait. There's more," said Corley, "but I need more coffee. Anybody else?"

By the time Kurt and Jim returned to Corley's office, Neal had retrieved a disposable plastic water bottle from his backpack, failing to see the two older men exchange a look of disapproval.

"So, where was I?" Corley wondered. "Oh, yes. Water wars and are they a possibility?"

"So … are they?" Jacobson asked as he moved toward the front of his seat.

"Well, in many ways, there are already water skirmishes underway," their mentor continued. "Some battles are taking place between individual citizens and corporations that have contaminated a shared water source. Other battles are between cattle ranchers and farmers. At any rate, experts are also warning, as our population grows and our planet warms, water will become increasingly scarce, and humans will inevitably start fighting over it."[13]

[12] http://www.nytimes.com/2012/08/24/us/midwest-water-wells-drying-up-in-drought.html?pagewanted=all
[13] Scientific American -- http://blogs.scientificamerican.com/cross-check/2012/03/26/are-we-doomed-to-wage-wars-over-water/

"Incredible," Jacobson said with a sigh. "Who could have dreamed such a nightmare?"

"Even now, water scarcity is not just a dream," Corley said. "In places like Saudi Arabia, where more than 60 percent of the population is under 25, compared to 30 percent in the U.S., the world is seeing the first collision between population growth and water supply at the regional level."[14]

"Well, why isn't anything being done about it?" the intern asked.

"There are efforts underway," confirmed Corley. "I read an article in the New York Times that said 'Like a Middle Eastern version of Las Vegas, Dubai's biggest challenge is water, which may be everywhere in the Gulf but is undrinkable without desalination plants.'[15]

"I then researched and found the United Arab Emirates (UAE), which includes Dubai, pumps nearly 14 percent of the world's desalinated water, or the equivalent of four billion, with a 'B,' bottles of water a day. Still though, the region only has about a four-day, backup supply of fresh water."

"Four days doesn't seem like much backup for 8 million people," Kurt commented, "considering the population of the UAE."

"You're right," agreed Corley. "Unfortunately, those desalination plants emit large amounts of carbon dioxide that have helped give Dubai and the other United Arab Emirates one of the world's largest carbon footprints. They also generate a great deal of heated sludge, which is pumped back into the sea."[16]

Corley studied his hands. "Ever heard of World Water Day?"

---

[14] www.guardian.co.uk/commentisfree/2011/apr/22/water-the-next-arab-battle
[15] www.nytimes.com/2010/10/28/business/energy-environment/28dubai.html?pagewanted=all&_r=0
[16] Ibid

"Not me," admitted Kurt.

"The United Nations and other international organizations organized World Water Day for the first time in 1993, and it's been held every March since to draw attention to water shortages. Initially, it was organized because drought and climate change already had disrupted water supplies around the globe.[17]

"Keep this event in mind for the future. But I want to get back to your question about water wars," Corley continued. "There is one organization called the Earth Policy Institute whose goal is to provide a roadmap to a sustainable future. The institute's president has argued for several years that climate change will undoubtedly disrupt already strained water supplies in many parts of the world … and, historically, droughts have been correlated with warfare.[18]

"U.S. intelligence agencies have also released a report stating that over the next decade 'water problems will contribute to instability in countries important to U.S. national security interests.'"[19]

"If intelligence agencies are already raising concern, there must be serious potential consequences," Jacobson said, taking another swig of water.

"As serious as running out of space in our landfills because of all the plastic water bottles people throw away every day," Corley stated.

The intern blushed. "Oh, this?" he said, holding up his water bottle. "It's a habit, I guess. Sorry. I'll make sure it goes into the recycle bin."

---

[17] www.unwater.org/watercooperation2013/

[18] Scientific American -- http://blogs.scientificamerican.com/cross-check/2012/03/26/are-we-doomed-to wage-wars-over-water/

[19] Scientific American -- http://blogs.scientificamerican.com/cross-check/2012/03/26/are-we-doomed-to wage-wars-over-water/

“That’s a good start,” Corley nodded approvingly. “But I have an even better solution. Remind me to give you a reusable bottle before you leave … just like the ones I gave Kurt and Raj during our first meeting.”

Kurt leaned back in his chair, wincing. “Did you really have to tell him that?” After the laughter quieted down, Kurt continued. “So, what I want to know is what corporations – specifically my employer – can do to help 1) conserve water and 2) stop pollution.”

“You may want to speak with my old friend Santos Silva,” said Corley. “He’s one of the top water conservationists in Rio de Janeiro.”

“Brazil? One of my friends and counterparts in the company, John Sullivan, is living in Rio now. I keep meaning to get back down there. Let me talk with my boss, the other Mr. Jacobson,” Kurt said, smiling. “I bet he would okay the two of you traveling down there with me as well. How about it, you guys? Want to come along?”

“I’m ready,” said Neal.

“Any time you’re ready,” Corley said enthusiastically. “Can’t think of a place I’d rather talk about environmental stewardship.”

Snapshot

Definitions

1. **24/7 Environmental Conversation** – Helpful feedback presented in a constructive manner to encourage someone to be aware of environmental stewardship and make environmentally friendly behaviors a way of life.
2. **Access** – A means of easily and comfortably approaching, entering, exiting, communicating with, or making use of.
3. **Conservation** – The act of conserving by saving, careful use, impacting positively or preventing injury, decay, waste, or loss.
4. **Delivery** – The process or the ability to move something from source to destination.
5. **Feedback** – Your response to witnessing an environmentally risky behavior. This feedback is positive, supportive and encouraging to the person you've observed.

Steps Toward Stewardship

Stop pollution by:

1. Avoiding unnecessary car trips. Combine errands into fewer trips and carpool whenever possible – to the grocery, school, after-school lessons, sports practice, church, etc. Walk or ride your bike whenever possible.
2. Learn more about taking care of the planet. Be open to new habits. Get ideas from the library, online, talks and lectures by experts … and don't forget about xeriscaping rather than watering your lawn.

3. Find small ways to save and/or conserve resources, i.e., lower wattage bulbs, low-flush toilets, turning off a light when an area is not in use.
4. Re-use whenever possible … and if you can't reuse, restore and/or recycle.
5. By reducing your use of disposables, such as shopping bags, paper towels, you'll not only save the planet but money as well.
6. Speak up. Be a role model, organize a neighborhood push to reduce, reuse, recycle and restore.
7. Try to do as much as you can online as you move to a totally paperless household, business or organization.

Additional Activities

1. Select any area where water conservation has become a priority. Find out what measures are being taken, why conservation is necessary and what the long-term outlook is.
2. Look at the number of plastic water bottles produced in 2005. What is that number for 2012? Over this period, why do you think this number has increased or decreased? Write a 300-word paper on your reasoning.
3. Because of a specific shortage of something in your area, write about how you either did without, did with less or replaced whatever was being restricted with something else. How did this shortage impact your long-range lifestyle?
4. Pick one conservation group, research their mission and discuss how this group and its efforts has helped the planet – or not.

Environmental Conversation Opportunities: It's in the (ECO) Cards

The following week, Kurt, Corley and Neal Jacobson boarded a jet for Rio. In order to offset the carbon footprint associated with their travel, the company had begun using the Carbon Footprint Calculator[1] to determine the cost of their travel on the environment. The associated funds were then donated to alternative energy or reforestation programs.

Once they'd stowed their carry-ons away and settled into their seats for takeoff, Neal opened a book and began reading. Kurt noticed that Neal continued reading as the pre-flight safety briefing began. Leaning over, Kurt whispered, "Can I ask you to watch this briefing for a minute?"

Puzzled by the request, Neal closed his book and focused his attention on what the flight attendant was saying.

At the conclusion of the briefing, Kurt began a 24/7 Safety Conversation: "I appreciate you remembering you had forgotten to

[1] www.carbonfootprint.com/calculator.aspx

turn off your cell phone before we took off, but what do you think concerned me about you reading during the pre-flight safety briefing?"

"I assume it was because I wasn't paying attention to what the flight attendant was saying," Neal responded somewhat defensively. "But I have flown enough to be able to give the flight attendant safety briefing and, believe me, if something were to happen, you would not be waiting for me to get out that emergency exit. Besides, look around. Did you see anyone else paying attention during the briefing?"

As he looked around, Kurt saw Neal's point. Many passengers were reading newspapers, several well into their books, two carrying on a conversation loud enough for the pilots to hear and a few already asleep. "Not sure how they do that," Kurt mumbled to himself. Then he pressed on: "What's wrong with not paying attention?"

Still a bit defensive, Neal responded. "Well, my 'bulletproof, it-can't-happen-to-me' attitude won't help in the unlikely event an incident was to occur."

"That's true," acknowledged Kurt. "But did you see that little girl sitting across the aisle from you?"

"Yes, I thought she was pretty young to be traveling by herself, but I would help her get off the plane, too, if anything happened," answered Neal, now less sure of the point Kurt was trying to make.

"Remember how we define a *safety culture* as the beliefs and behaviors passed along from one generation to the next ...?" Kurt queried.

"Sure, and we create this culture by what we, personally, demonstrate as well as what we reward and tolerate in other people ..." Neal's voice trailed off as he began to realize the seriousness of his at-risk behavior of not paying attention to the flight attendant.

"I'm guessing you are beginning to understand the message passed on to the child sitting next to you – that it's okay not to pay attention when it comes to safety – sets the wrong example and just perpetuates a poor safety culture?" Kurt asked.

"I am," Neal confirmed, "and I really appreciate you continuing to model the 24/7 Safety Conversation.[2] If the company can continue using that, plus incorporate the 24/7 Environmental Conversation, we would be miles ahead of our competitors in terms of safety, environmentalism and, no doubt, production!"

"Right you are and, along with learning what it takes to be an environmental steward, I've been strategizing how to build the corporate culture we need … so I'd like to show you the rough outline of how I envision this all working. Of course, I'm open to your suggestions," Kurt said.

As the two men looked over what Kurt had compiled, he continued his narrative, using the bulleted points on the sheets:

> "In order for our organization to become stewards of our environment, our beliefs and behaviors – individually and as a group – must change."

"Like we were talking about in the break room, beliefs drive behaviors that drive results," Neal pointed out.

"Exactly," Kurt responded, "Or moving environmentalism from our heads, to our hearts, to our hands, or in the case of the 24/7 Environmental Conversation, our mouths. That means having the courage to speak up when you observe people potentially harming the environment or wasting valuable resources."

---

[2] Anderson and Lorber: *Safety 24/7*

"That 24/7 aspect can't be overstated. We have to be willing to speak to anyone, from a manager, to a co-worker, to a friend or family member … anyone," Corley emphasized.

"Right you are, Jim. Essentially, our first step is to look for **E**nvironmental **C**onversation **O**pportunities or **ECO**s," explained Kurt.

"Like we had the other day, when we met, right?" Neal wondered. "Obviously it made an impression on me, but what about the rest of the company?

Kurt knew he had made the right choice in Neal. "Here, take a look at this. It's something I put together to help people know what to look for as well as say and, if a company wants to, they can use this to keep track of ECOs. Here's what the front of the card would look like:"

Environmental Conversation Opportunity Card

Location .... Date ....

❑ Condition ❑ Behavioral

✓ Check Only One Box

❑ Positive ❑ Planning

❑ Communications ❑ Tools & Equipment

❑ Procedures ❑ Housekeeping

✓ Check Only One Box

What was observed and discussed?

What action is recommended?

What action has been taken or agreement made?

Observation submitted by Name/Position (Optional)

Corrective Action approved by Name/Position

Date Corrective Action carried out

"And here is what the back of the card would look like," Kurt said, handing each man another card.

ECO Checklist

Reactions of People When Observed

- ❑ Changing plan
- ❑ Rearranging the job
- ❑ Adjust or add equipment

Personal Protection Equipment (PPE)

- ❑ Head & face
- ❑ Ears, eyes, feet
- ❑ Lungs, skin, hands

Tools & Equipment

- ❑ Right job
- ❑ Used correctly

Procedures & Standards

- ❑ Established
- ❑ Adequate
- ❑ Understood
- ❑ Maintained

ECO-friendly Questions

- ✦ Can you tell me about your job?
- ✦ What could go wrong?
- ✦ How could you hurt the environment?
- ✦ How serious?
- ✦ How could you prevent it?
- ✦ Who else could be affected?
- ✦ What if the unexpected happened?
- ✦ What concerned me when I first saw you?
- ✦ Why do you think I stopped you?
- ✦ How can the job be done with greater care for the environment?

"What a great way to teach – and remind – your people!" Corley exclaimed.

"Thanks, I appreciate you saying that," replied Kurt. "By carrying these cards, we can stop and take advantage of these opportunities, wherever and whenever they occur. So, let's keep going, talking about ECOs and stewardship, I mean. Our next step is as follows:

1. To maintain and support a clear vision of environmental stewardship, each one of us must mentally practice identifying our own behaviors that put the environment at risk."

"When we become aware of a specific behavior, we can apply that behavior to a variety of situations and see how it can impact the environment in multiple aspects of our life," Corley translated.

"So, my environmentally risky behavior – leaving the water running in the break room – can be applied in my house, outside while washing my car, wherever," said Neal, seeming pleased with his insight.

"Or, at the hotel we'll be using in Rio," added Kurt.

"Or restaurants where the wait staff doesn't automatically serve water," Corley pointed out.

"And to take your vision of environmental stewardship to the next level, what if you knew – for example – that it takes 1,800 gallons of water to grow enough cotton to make a single pair of jeans?[3] Would it be worthwhile to you to wear those jeans a bit longer or recycle them?"

"Wow! I never thought of jeans from that perspective," Neal admitted.

[3] www.treehugger.com/clean-technology/how-many-gallons-of-water-does-it-take-to-make.html

"And that's probably why you also may not realize it takes 1,799 gallons of water to make one pound of ground beef,"[4] Kurt continued.

"So, if you raise a cow that weighs 1,000 pounds?" the younger man wondered aloud.

"You'd need enough water to float a very large boat," Corley completed his thought, smiling.

"Gee, that's definitely a new way of thinking. Guess I'll think more about how what I'm wearing or eating impacts our environment," Neal concluded.

"Which is exactly what this second point is all about," explained Kurt. "On to our next step:

2. Using the Performance ABCs – Activator, Behavior, Consequence – we need to clearly communicate the goals of being environmental stewards, follow up to see how people are progressing and pointing out their positive results.

"Tell me about the ABCs," Neal requested, looking rather confused. "They don't sound like anything I learned in kindergarten."

"I'm glad you asked," Kurt continued. "I have a friend named Sam who is a world-class safety guru," he began. "To better explain the Performance ABCs, he showed me three pictures of his little granddaughter, who was just learning to walk."

Kurt took a sip of coffee and continued. "The first picture shows Sam, standing with the little girl and holding her hands above her head. The camera captured her reaching out with her right foot to take a step.

[4] www.treehugger.com/clean-technology/how-many-gallons-of-water-does-it-take-to-make.html

"In the second photo, you see Sam has let go of her hands and she seems to be in motion, and the third picture shows the little girl sitting in her grandpa's lap, eating a cookie," Kurt said. "Those pictures illustrate the Performance ABCs."

"If you'll pardon my play on words, I think I'm getting the picture," Neal laughed.

Kurt was pleased. Neal was, indeed, a fast learner. "Okay, so here's what Sam taught me. In the first photo, she was gripping her grandpa's hands to keep from falling. Sam's being there and offering something to hold onto provided his granddaughter with the Activator."

"And the Activator is like gaining confidence to do something you haven't done before. Am I right?" asked Neal, eagerly.

"Like you said, you're getting the picture," Kurt encouraged. "In the second photo, the little girl was no longer holding his hands but was trying to take a step or two on her own. That's Behavior. Now that she knew what to do and had confidence to do it, she was ready to venture further out of her comfort zone and step out alone."

"I'm with you so far," Neal confirmed. "What's the third photo about?"

"The Consequence photo showed the little girl enjoying cookies and milk with her grandpa, which was the reward for working hard and finally succeeding.

"Okay, I totally get it," Neal exclaimed rather proudly. "When you're building a culture of environmental stewardship, you set clear goals or standards with your team."

"Exactly," Corley chimed in. "Then, periodically, you look to see how they are progressing toward those goals, gently make corrections when needed and then, once the goal is realized, you must make sure they understand the results of their efforts and reward them. Regardless of who you are working with, we all respond well to the Performance ABCs."

"Okay, we ready for the next point?" asked Kurt.

3. As we're working to change the culture, we need to, as the old song goes, *Accentuate the Positive.*

Neal looked puzzled. "We use the phrase 'accentuate the positive' as we move into a culture of environmental stewardship as a reminder to notice when people are doing something right," Kurt explained. "For example, do you remember what I praised you for when we first met in the break room?"

"Sure, you thanked me for wiping the countertop," came Neal's quick reply.

"That's right," confirmed Kurt. "You remembered our conversation because of the praise you received, and you will continue to repeat the behavior, even when I am not there."

"Got it," Neal said. "And I assume 'accentuating the positive' works when it comes to safety as well?"

Corley jumped in. "Accentuating the positive works with safety, environmental stewardship and, of course, operations, which is why we say safety, environmentalism and operations are 'interdependent.' You show me a safe and environmentally sound operation and I can guarantee, it will be a productive operation. They all go hand-in-hand."

"That brings us to 'redirect and provide a positive consequence,'" Kurt smiled. "I know this one works because I've had a supervisor redirect me in the past … and I'll bet you two have, as well.

4. When it comes to environmental stewardship, 'redirect' means when you see someone doing something that puts the environment at risk, you recognize it as an Environmental Conversation Opportunity and help them understand the potential consequences of their behavior.

By following these four steps, you can motivate anyone of any age to want to change their behavior for a more positive outcome.

"So, how do I apply them at the corporate office? You make it sound so easy," asked Neal.

"You'd be surprised just how easy it is," Corley said. "I mean, who do you know who wants to turn on a tap and have no water, or flip a switch and have no electrical power, because there's too little water to generate hydroelectric power or a shortage of clean air? I mean, nobody wants to be the cause of our entire society taking a step back into the dark ages … and that's what we're talking about here."

"Makes total sense to me, but it takes looking at our world a bit differently, doesn't it?" Neal replied after a long silence.

"Let's get back to that point when we've completed our visit," the older man suggested.

Later, as the aircraft banked in preparing to land, Kurt was captivated by the deep azure of the water contrasted by the creamy white sands of the shoreline below. At the same time, he wondered if this beautiful scene would, at some point, find its place on the planet's growing list of "endangered species."

✦ ✦ ✦ ✦ ✦

Like most airports around the world, Rio's was crowded and busy. After the men cleared immigration, a familiar voice – one with a broad Australian accent – boomed out, "Over here, mates!" It was Kurt's old friend John Sullivan. "It's been a while, Kurt, but you're looking good for an old man," he teased as the two men shook hands.

"Good to see you, John. It's been too long, but I'm glad to see you're looking well. How's the family?"

"Luckily, I've kept myself out of the hospital," he chuckled remembering Kurt's visit to his hospital bedside several years earlier following a car accident, "and Theresa's as beautiful and quirky as ever."

"And Ethan?"

"Oh, he's doing all the good," John beamed. "In his last year of medical school and just completing an internship in the bloody Outback."

Kurt congratulated his friend. "Hey, I almost forgot. Jim Corley and Neal Jacobson, meet John Sullivan, one of the best of our international management team."

After exchanging greetings, the four loaded into John's car for the trip to their hotel, the Copacabana Palace located close to Copacabana, Ipanema and Arpoador beaches.

"So, mates," commented John as he followed the trio of visitors into the hotel, "You can see why I chose to put you up at this place. Three of the world's most beautiful beaches, filled with some of the world's most beautiful women."

"Like we're going to have time to spend on the beach," Kurt said wryly. "Remember, we're here on business."

Sullivan surveyed the group as Kurt spoke. "Well, maybe you can find a few hours to slip away and relax. But it's true. The women here are beautiful and they come from around the globe." He winked at Neal as the other men laughed at the thought.

"In the meantime, after you blokes have checked in, meet me in the hotel restaurant," John suggested. "It's well-known for several dishes, but their tiramisu is my favorite dessert."

When Kurt, Corley and Neal joined John Sullivan in the hotel lobby a half hour later, Corley looked around expectantly. "Ah, there you are, my friend!" he exclaimed as a well-dressed gentleman walked their way. "Meet Dr. Santos Silva," Corley said after greeting the man.

"So glad to meet all of you. Welcome to Brazil," said the man in a deep, well-modulated voice.

"Santos taught me everything I know about hydrology," Corley began as they were all seated in the large dining room. "I took the liberty of having him join us for dinner so he could bring us all up to date about the state of water quality and water supply in this part of the world."

"Santos, we welcome you, not only for your knowledge of hydrology, but also to help me figure out this menu," Kurt said.

"With pleasure," Santos said, slightly bowing. "I'll do my best."

After enjoying a wonderful meal of Brazilian dishes, the five men sat, talking and finishing their desserts and coffee. "Definitely one of the best dinners of my lifetime," Kurt said, "but I noticed we had to ask for water with dinner. Is there a water shortage here in Rio?"

Silva took a moment to answer. "I can truthfully say, there is no shortage of water here right now," he said. "But, there was a study published a few years ago by our national water agency that predicted a shortage of water by 2015, basically due to population growth."[5]

"I just assumed Brazil was a water powerhouse," Neal admitted.

"We are," the hydrologist replied, "but if investment isn't made to meet the growing demand for water, there's a possibility 55 percent of Brazil's municipalities will experience water shortages – and that includes many of our large cities.

"But isn't Brazil blessed with natural springs and the largest aquifer in the world?" Now it was Neal's turn to ask questions.

"As you point out, our Guarani Aquifer is the largest underground water reserve in the world," Silva paused. "However, there continues to be a large population growth, more industry and more international companies coming into this country, not to mention Brazil is host for the World Cup in 2014 and the Summer Olympics in 2016 – and every one of these factors increases the demand for water."

"So, aside from investment, what's the rest of the plan?" asked Corley.

"The government has begun some initiatives to address the problem of supply, but we also have a pollution problem, particularly in some of the *favelas*," Silva said, using a word from Brazil's national language of Portuguese which means 'shantytown.'

"As slowly as government typically moves, it would surprise me if they beat the five-year projections with successful interventions. In the meantime, some states in Brazil are charging a bulk water tax, but it's not consistent across the board … and people who live in the cities also pay for water, sewage and garbage disposal."

[5] www.portal2014.org.br/en/news/6567/HALF+OF+ALL+BRAZILIAN+CITIES+WILL+SUFFER+FROM+LACK+OF+WATER+IN+2015.html

Neal had just taken his last bite of tiramisu. "Has desalination ever been discussed as an option?"

"Oh, absolutely. It's been going on for several years here." Silva took a moment to signal the waiter for the check. "In Brazil, we have two issues – clean water and sanitation.[6] So, the government has many contractors working in these areas. Now, in the popular *turista* areas, like Rio, there are few issues," he reassured, "but in the smaller towns and rural areas, the problems continue … and, I might add, the demand for reverse osmosis equipment in Brazil has grown exponentially."[7]

"I'd like to see one of those systems at work," Corley mentioned.

"Tomorrow we'll have a full day talking to some hydrologists and taking a closer look at desalination," John interjected, "but for now, let's call it a night."

"Great idea," Kurt chimed in. "I've never had much luck sleeping during a flight. I want to thank our host, Dr. Silva, for a wonderful evening of delicious food and informative conversation."

"Until tomorrow, then, mates." After shaking hands with the three men, John accompanied Silva to his car and invited him to join the group on their tour the next morning.

"I'd be honored," said the hydrologist, "but I'm due to fly to Venezuela tomorrow."

"Venezuela? Are they facing similar shortages like we are here in Brazil?" John asked.

"Some blame the water shortage from a few years ago on El Nino and the lack of rain," Silva said, "and that could easily explain away

[6] www.un.org/waterforlifedecade/human_right_to_water.shtml
[7] http://gwri-ic.technion.ac.il/pdf/IDS/103.pdf

part of the problem, but the failure to invest in hydrology systems and aqueducts has made it difficult to expand power production enough to meet the current demand."

John Sullivan thought for a moment. "So, there it is again. As long as things are going along okay, municipalities – even entire countries – ignore the environment, don't plan for the future and don't change behaviors or usage patterns. When a crisis occurs, people definitely aren't ready but, even more, they're totally surprised when power outages occur or nothing comes out of the water spigot."

"Sad but true," Silva agreed.

John extended his hand. "Goodnight, my friend."

The older man bowed slightly, "*Boa Noite.*"

Bright and early the next morning, John Sullivan and his trio of visitors set out to see one of the area's most-respected hydrologists, Oswaldo Costa. As they drove up to the technology center, the Americans were impressed with the modern facility, located several miles from Rio on a spacious campus.

"It seems to go on forever," Neal volunteered.

Oswaldo Costa was a tall, thin man with a shock of once-black hair. He greeted John and the other guests warmly and escorted them to his office. A tray with a carafe of coffee and cups was centered on an impressive wooden conference table.

Kurt opened the discussion with a brief narrative about his environmental stewardship project. Costa listened intently and then offered an overview of his own area.

"As you know," he began, "there are many technologies now available for water treatment. Initially, reverse osmosis was used, beginning back in the 1960s, to treat brackish water as well as desalination of seawater.[8]

"Later, it was consolidated with other water treatment re-use technologies," he continued. "Now it is possible to use this technology to produce drinking water as well as industrial-use water from wastewater effluent."[9]

The look on Neal's face likely mirrored the other men's thoughts. Costa smiled. "To give you some idea of the product, the water used to make this coffee is from our water re-use system."

Trying not to insult his host, the younger man gently set his cup down on the table.

"Don't worry, my young friend," Costa attempted to reassure him. "Several of your country's larger cities as well as cities around the world are using – or will soon be using – this or similar technologies."

"Bet you won't find that information in the tourist brochures," the younger man said, "although I'll have to admit, I was enjoying the coffee."

"Actually, the so-called 'yuck factor' that goes along with reclaimed or recycled water goes away quickly, particularly if drinkers have the choice of recycled water or no water coming out of their taps at home," Kurt said.

"I recently visited the world's largest water recycling plant in Orange County, California," Costa offered. "They have a four-year-old system

---

[8] www.eetcorp.com/heepm/RO_ReviewE.pdf
[9] http://gwri-ic.technion.ac.il/pdf/IDS/103.pdf

that replenishes the groundwater basin with 70 million gallons of treated effluent daily – or about 20 percent of the content of the aquifer.[10]

"There are other sites, too, like the ones in El Paso, Texas, and some areas around Los Angeles," he continued. "Now, I will say much of the recycled water is used in industrial plants or watering sports fields, but some of it also goes into the drinking water supply as well."

"So, what are the water-quality people saying?" asked Neal, now somewhat recovered from his initial shock.

"I can answer that one," Corley volunteered. "A new analysis from the National Academy of Science suggests the risk from drinking reused water 'does not appear to be any higher, and may be orders of magnitude lower' than any risk from conventional treatment."[11]

Costa looked at his watch. "My, time is passing so quickly," he murmured and excused himself from the room, returning to distribute hardhats and safety glasses before taking the visitors on a tour of the water recycling plant.

"As you might realize, the growing scarcity of water supplies is changing every aspect of hydrology as we know it, not to mention municipal, industrial and agricultural water practices," he explained as the five of them stood on a bridge over a tank of effluent.

"So, it's only a matter of time before all of us will be getting reclaimed water from our taps at home," said Neal, beginning to see the big picture.

"It would be fair to say that," Costa agreed. "What once was a last resort is now being more easily embraced and acceptance is spreading."

[10] www.acwa.com/

[11] www.nytimes.com/2012/02/10/science/earth/despite-yuck-factor-treated-wastewater-used-for-drinking.html?pagewanted=all&_r=0

"If this is the case, will our water costs go up or down since we're on the verge of using recycled water universally?" Kurt wondered.

Costa answered this question as the group made its way back to his office.

"Here's what I know … the Orange County plant cost $481 million. Its reclaimed water costs $1.80 per thousand gallons when regional water subsidies are factored in. Without these subsidies, reclaimed water's cost was 14 percent less than desalinated water, and desalination required three to 10 times the energy output. When compared to simply tapping into local groundwater or aquifers, water recycling costs about 60 percent more in California. In El Paso, it costs four times more. Most people see this as the price to pay to keep groundwater sustainable."[12]

As the men were saying their goodbyes, Kurt's cell phone rang. He excused himself from the group and returned a few minutes later. His expression was difficult to interpret. "That was Jessica. She's at the hospital and her mother is in critical condition," he managed. I need to get back."

Jim Corley also had difficulty speaking. "Janet, your mother-in-law? What happened?"

"Don't know the details. Just need to get back," Kurt said, hurriedly gathering his papers.

"I'll ask my assistant to make your reservations," Costa offered.

"Oh, that would be a great help," Corley said. "We would appreciate it."

[12] www.nytimes.com/2012/02/10/science/earth/despite-yuck-factor-treated-wastewater-used-for-drinking.html?pagewanted=all&_r=0

"And I'll drive you over to the hotel so you can pack your things," John offered.

"I'm sorry to hear about your mother-in-law. Is there anything I can do to help?" Neal said as he helped Kurt load his luggage into a taxi.

"Just say a prayer for her," responded Kurt quietly. And, just like that, their trip to Brazil came to an end.

SNAPSHOT

DEFINITIONS

1. **Desalination** – Any of several processes to remove some amount of salt and other minerals from saline water. Saltwater is desalinated to produce fresh water suitable for human consumption or irrigation.
2. **Effluent** – Defined by the United States Environmental Protection Agency as "wastewater (treated or untreated) that flows out of a treatment plant, sewer, or industrial outfall. Generally refers to wastes discharged into surface waters." The Compact Oxford English Dictionary defines effluent as "liquid waste or sewage discharged into a river or the sea."
3. **Environmental Conversation Opportunity** – The courage to speak up when you observe people potentially harming the environment or wasting valuable resources, pointing out the issue and, together, coming to an agreement about how to avoid or improve the behavior in the future.
4. **Environmental Conversation Opportunity (ECO) cards** – Specially designed cards to use during an Environmental Conversation Opportunity to track, teach and remind co-workers about environmental stewardship. These cards are available through the SOPHIE Says website: www.sophiesays.org
5. **Reverse-osmosis** – Membrane separation processes that operate without heating and therefore use less energy than conventional thermal separation processes (distillation, Sublimation or crystallization). This separation process is purely physical and because it is a gentle process, both fractions (permeate and retentate) can be used.

CONCEPTS

1. **The Performance ABCs**: **A**ctivator, **B**ehavior, **C**onsequence. This means to clearly communicate your goals and follow up to see how your team, department and/or corporation are progressing. Once the goal is achieved, make certain the group is praised for their progress and achievement.

2. **Accentuate the positive**: Notice when people are doing something right. Praise is always a strong motivator. Responding to positive reinforcement or feedback is a human characteristic.

3. **To change a behavior, redirect**: If a person is not focused on the established goal, redirect him/her and then provide a positive consequence once the secondary goal is achieved.

4. **For real change to occur, behaviors must change**. (Ours included.)

5. **Environmentally risky behaviors affect many more people than just those in the immediate vicinity.** The impact is much like the ripple effect, far-reaching and ever-widening.

STEPS TOWARD STEWARDSHIP

To demonstrate your buy-in to environmental stewardship:

1. Support environmental awareness and stewardship as a core value by committing to put human survival on this planet ahead of all other demands.

2. Accountability gives every employee the right and responsibility to call a timeout if any operation or practice is damaging to the environment, or if a practice can be improved by reusing, reducing, recycling and restoring. It also rewards employees for calling a timeout, even if it's a false alarm.

3. Follow-up involves demonstrating and communicating a personal commitment to environmental stewardship in all your actions.

4. Elevate those who support the culture of environmental stewardship; those who don't embrace this core value should be eliminated.

5. Continue to emphasize Environmental Conversation Opportunities (ECO), serve as an ECO role model and help train new employees to observe behaviors that are harmful to the environment and to have effective ECOs.

Saving Water in the Yard

1. Use native or drought-tolerant plants.

2. Water during the night to avoid evaporation.

3. Ensure that sprinkler heads only water what they're supposed to be watering (i.e. not sidewalks, driveway, etc.).

4. Reduce two minutes off a sprinkler system's run time, which can save 80 gallons of water.

5. Use drip irrigation in beds and around trees to get water to the roots and greatly reduce evaporation.

6. Apply one inch of water to the lawn every seven days during the summer.

7. Water only every 15-20 days during the winter.

8. Capture rainwater from your home's roof. One inch of rain from a 1,000- square-foot roof yields about 600 gallons of water.

ADDITIONAL ACTIVITIES

1. Choose one day over a weekend, during semester break or over summer vacation and see how little water you can use during one 24-hour period. Without becoming dehydrated, see how much you can do on a little water. Those living in areas where wells have dried up due to drought say they can take a shower, brush their teeth and wash their hair and still have a little left over from one gallon of water. (Hint: Water reuse is encouraged.)
2. If a plastic bottle-recycling program isn't in effect at your campus or your workplace, find out how to develop one. Once the recycling effort is underway, make signs and place them in various areas where people congregate as reminders of the program and its importance to the environment.
3. Study the recent impact of the 2012 drought in the United States. After evaluating the devastating effects of the drought, determine which region was most affected and how life has changed in that area.
4. Scientists believe 30 or more states in the U.S. will or already experience water shortages. Develop a plan to lessen the impact on lifestyles in one of these states.
5. Develop a brief (1,000 words) paper on how changes in water levels of the Mississippi River impact people living close to the river as well as those living in other states.
6. The Texas Water Star Program has been introduced to encourage water-saving habits. Analyze and evaluate this program for states with shrinking water supplies and expanding populations. Then report your findings, along with any other water-saving strategies, to increase individual participation in the program.

First, Convert the Leaders; Then Comes the Bigger Challenge

Kurt Bradshaw reached the automatic doors of the hospital and then stopped, looked around and spotted the information desk. By the time he reached the desk, Jim Corley had caught up. "Good thing I hit the treadmill regularly," he said trying to catch his breath.

As Kurt gave the woman at the counter his mother-in-law's name, Jim retrieved his handkerchief and was wiping his face. "This way, Jim," Kurt directed. "She's in the Intensive Care Unit, 11th floor."

As the elevator doors opened, Jessica immediately saw her husband and ran to hug him. "Oh, I'm so glad you're here. You, too, Jim. But, she's not doing well … the doctors are trying everything …."

Kurt hugged his wife tightly for several moments. "I'm here now," he whispered, "so tell me what happened … heart attack, stroke?"

"Let's go sit down near the nurses' station," Jessica said.

A hospital volunteer had seen the two men accompany Jessica to the family waiting area and brought a tray of coffee. "Mother had gone to the coast to volunteer with Hilda and Gretchen, her friends from the local Environmental Club. Jim, you know both of them, I'm sure," she said.

Corley nodded. "Together, those three are the engine that drives the club here."

Jessica continued. "The Conservancy was holding a sea turtle hatchling release on the coast and needed volunteers. It sounds like a big mistake now, but even though it was raining at the time, Mother decided not to wear her shoes on the beach because sand had gotten into them the day before."

"Okay, so what happened?" Kurt put his arm around her, reassuringly, adding, "Your mother is strong."

Jessica brushed away a tear. "As she was releasing one of the nests of hatchlings, she stepped on something sharp in the surf," his wife said. "Mother first thought it might just be a rock, a shell, or maybe even a jellyfish sting. When she looked down to see what it was, she found she had stepped on a hypodermic needle, partially buried in the sand … possibly biowaste that constantly washes ashore."

Kurt was silent for a moment. "So, did she get treated?"

"Of course … but only after she had released the nests of baby turtles she had been assigned. You know how she is."

"You mean she waited?"

"Only 30 minutes or so," Jessica responded, wiping her eyes. "She thought it was nothing … just a scratch."

Jim Corley had been quiet up to this point but now couldn't mask his concern.

"You said it had rained the night before?"

Jessica turned to the older man. "Yes, but why are you asking, Jim?"

"During even a brief period after a rain, the State Health Department advises the public not to swim or surf in coastal waters because they have been freshly polluted with urban runoff – including sewage. In heavily urbanized areas, the coastal water, after a rain, has high concentrations of bacteria as well as pesticides, fertilizers, heavy metals and other chemicals.[1]

"Some counties issue 72-hour beach advisories, but – unfortunately – they don't all post signs," Corley said, looking rather helpless.

"The doctors told me she's contracted some type of infection," the daughter continued, "but they don't know whether it came from the needle, the water or …."

"Mrs. Bradshaw, you can go in, but only for a few minutes," a nurse explained.

Kurt shook his head. "This can't be happening to Janet." Then he took a breath. "If the Health Department doesn't want surfers in the water, I don't want to think about what this bacteria could do to an older person … isn't a staph infection pretty vicious?"

"Vicious isn't the word," Corley said. "If we're talking urban runoff, we're dealing with streptococcus bacteria, E. Coli and … well, just about any other 'bug' you can name."

[1] www.surfline.com/community/whoknows/whoknows.cfm?id=1157

When Jessica returned from seeing her mother, her expression said everything. "She's so sick. The doctor came in, saying the antibiotics they started need more time before we can tell if they're working. In the meantime, they're concerned about her slipping into a coma and they're doing everything they can to prevent pneumonia as well."

"We need to stay positive," Corley said, sounding more like a father than a friend, "and in my book, a little food now and then also helps."

"I'd like to stay close by for now," Kurt's wife responded. "I don't want to miss a chance to see Mother, whenever they'll allow me."

Although he had offered to stay with her, Jessica had known how tired Kurt must be after flying back from Brazil, so she sent him home while she kept an overnight vigil at her mother's bedside.

Unable to sleep, Kurt arrived at his office earlier than usual the next morning, eager to discuss what he learned in Brazil with his team. At long last, he felt he was making progress.

"Jacobson," answered the voice at the other end of the phone. After a brief conversation, Kurt took the elevator to his boss's office.

"Before we get to your plan," the CEO began, "first, let me say our prayers are with your mother-in-law. Please let me know if you need anything."

"Thanks, Mr. Jacobson. The doctors tell Jess her mother isn't reacting as badly to the bacteria as they were expecting, so they see that as a positive sign," Kurt said.

"I want to thank you for selecting my nephew for your team," Jacobson continued. "He's become so passionate about environmental stewardship, it's hard to believe it's only been a few weeks."

"That seems to be the way it works," Kurt agreed. "Especially when you know you have an opportunity to make a positive change whether in the environment or, as you know, in safety."

"So, let's talk about what you've learned, and planned, thus far." Fred Jacobson seemed eager, which Kurt saw as a sign of senior management's continued support.

Sliding an Environmental Conversation Opportunity card across the table, Kurt gave his boss a few moments to examine it. "I want to begin with this ECO card, which will serve a dual purpose for us. First, I would like to make it available for sale on the SOPHIE Says website (www.sophiesays.org)."

"And would we make these available to other companies, even our competitors?" asked Jacobson. Before Kurt could answer, the man across the table answered his own question. "Of course we would. Forget I asked. When it comes to environmental stewardship, we all must be on the same team."

"I agree!" Kurt responded enthusiastically, "So, I'd like to begin building our culture of environmental stewardship by helping our employees realize what we just discussed: Environmental stewardship begins with everyone in this company. Our planet is home for all of us, and if we all remain aware of its importance, we'll be making a good first step."

"Absolutely," said Jacobson, "and, our employees must understand that taking care of our environment is a priority here."

Kurt was thoughtful before he spoke. "Mr. Jacobson, we have a number of priorities within the company, but what would happen if I asked you to rank them?"

Jacobson rubbed his chin thoughtfully. "I see where you are headed."

"Yes sir, environmental stewardship must be more than a priority that management expects employees to embrace," Kurt explained. "Instead, it must be a core value within this organization."

"Core value," Jacobson repeated. "Hmmm."

"Remember what we've learned from making safety a core value," Kurt continued. "If safety – or in this case, environmental stewardship – is simply a new priority, it could take a backseat when budgets, operational performance or client demands become an issue."

"Oh, believe me," said the CEO, "I've seen it happen dozens of times. As senior managers, our intentions are good, but when push comes to shove ...."

"We get the job done, no matter what we have to sacrifice. That's how it happens in most companies," Kurt agreed. "But, when we make environmental stewardship a core value, we're saying – to our employees and to our customers – we put the environment above all other demands."

"Except, of course, safety, which becomes *the* priority if it comes into conflict with one of our other core values," emphasized Jacobson. "And, before you say anything, it is not all about policies and procedures. It's about our people."

Kurt saw the CEO had begun making notes. "Correct, so our first step is to encourage our people to take personal responsibility for the environment in which they work and live. We help them understand they share this planet with people they don't even know, so everything they do – or don't do – to maintain a healthy environment impacts people in other cities, states and countries around the world."

"And, just like safety, what they do or don't do will impact the next generation. This definitely makes sense," said Jacobson, continuing to write. "So, what's our first step, as you see it?"

Kurt moved to the next page of his plan. "First, let's take a look at some of the cost savings associated with adopting environmental stewardship as a core value. ... According to Rich Lechner, Vice President of Environment and Energy at IBM, '... more stringent environmental policies allow companies to discover wasteful and oftentimes expensive routines that were buried under years of business. Eliminating them can help a company cut down on costs while also becoming more environmentally friendly. IBM, for example, found for every $1 in energy savings, the company saves an additional $6 to $8 in operational savings.'"[2]

"Very impressive," Jacobson said. "So if your so-called behavior-based environmental stewardship can reduce costs, I'm all in."

"Ready for Step One?" asked Kurt.

"Absolutely."

"First, I'd like to hold some discussions with our middle management around the country, and I think we can do that through teleconferences rather than traveling place to place," Kurt explained. "During these meetings, I would like to introduce them to the Environmentally Conscious Opportunities concept."

Kurt slid a drawing across the table.

[2] www.ibm.com/smarterplanet/global/files/br__pt_br__buildings__CIW03052USEN_HR.pdf

Jacobson looked up after studying the drawing for a few seconds. "Looks interesting, but now tell me about it."

"I call it the Three C's ... Conservation, Condition, and Conversation," began Kurt. "Let's start with Conservation. There are multiple times throughout our day where we have the opportunity to demonstrate Conservation, whether it's doing something like using less water, recycling, or just turning out the light when we leave a room. Each of us needs to get in the habit of consciously looking for opportunities to conserve."

"That seems clear and easy enough," remarked the CEO.

"Well, then there is Condition," continued Kurt. "This asks us to consider a Condition that might negatively impact the environment, such as: are there storm drains near a construction project, am I using the correct chemical for the job I'm doing, or taking into consideration actual environmental conditions like wind and rain that could impact the job?"

"Okay, so Condition is not so much about the people as it is about what they are doing or using and/or the environmental Condition that exists when they are performing a task. Am I correct in my thinking?" asked Jacobson.

"Right you are," responded Kurt. "Finally, there is Conversation, which is similar to the Safety 24/7 Conversation we use in order to provide someone specific feedback."

"It certainly looks and sounds as though you have put a lot of time and effort into ways our company can become more environmentally responsible. But speaking of looks, it appears to me you haven't slept much in the last few days, so why don't you take the rest of the day and get some sleep," Jacobson suggested.

"Thanks, but I would rather not, if that's okay" said Kurt. "Working takes my mind off Janet, and I'll check in at the hospital during my lunch hour."

"Then, if you have the energy, I would like to hear more about the process you've come up with. What follows step one?" inquired the CEO.

"Step two," smiled Kurt.

Jacobson laughed. "Glad to see you still have your sense of humor."

"They say laughter is the best medicine," Kurt responded. "Anyway, after step one, we'll demonstrate how to conduct those Conversations and elicit feedback and commitments."

"Sounds good … and then what?" Jacobson wanted to know.

"Next, as management guru Ken Blanchard[3] emphasized in his books, we get our managers to 'catch our employees doing something

[3] http://howwelead.org/

right' … and then reward them for their positive impact on the environment and make them feel valued."

Jacobson smiled at Kurt's enthusiasm. "It should help that I agree with you in that we need to make environmental stewardship a core value," the CEO said. "When doing so, we'll also look to promote employees who clean up the way they do things, suggest better operational strategies to cut down on waste, conserve resources or reuse materials, even if it slows us down a bit or perhaps costs a little more in the short term."

"That is great news, Mr. Jacobson. Elevating environmentalism to a core value is one of the best things a company can do to help ensure the process continues to move forward," Kurt confirmed.

"Just like when it comes to at-risk behavior, step three is giving each and every employee the right, and responsibility, to stop an operation if they see it is actually, or even potentially, going to damage the environment … and, what's more, rather than being punished for stopping the operation, the employee will be rewarded for having the courage to speak up," Kurt continued.

"Ouch … and if you'll pardon the pun, I know stopping the job has been key to improving our safety culture, but I guess I hadn't thought about stopping a job over an environmental issue," Jacobson thought out loud.

"You're right, it is easy to see why we tell our employees they can stop the job when it comes to safety," exclaimed Kurt, "but if a company is going to truly step up to the plate and make environmentalism a core value, then they have to make environmental stewardship a condition of employment, and all of that goes with it, like personal responsibility and accountability."

"Anybody?" Jacobson tested. "Even my nephew?"

"Anybody," Kurt smiled at Jacobson's try at humor.

"And when do you want to begin the managers' workshops?" asked the CEO.

"What about next week?" came Kurt's response.

Jacobson smiled. "You sure do move quickly."

Kurt nodded. "You're not the first Jacobson to have told me that. In all seriousness though, we don't have any more time to waste."

Later that day, while Raj and Neal Jacobson III were working on scheduling the teleconferences, Kurt's phone rang.

After a brief conversation, Kurt joined his assistants in the adjoining office. "Want to hear something pretty amazing?"

Raj and Neal turned their focus away from their computer screens.

"Just had a call from a friend who shared a story about a girl's 13- and 14-year-old volleyball team in The Woodlands,[4] all of whom refused to shower for an entire week," Kurt continued. "But get this, they were doing it for a cause and raised close to $5,000 in less than seven days."

"Okay," Raj relented. "I'm impressed … but it's simply because I have a sister who wouldn't dream of going without washing her hair daily. So, what motivated this smelly project?" he joked.

"He said the girls' 'shower strike' was part of a national effort to raise

[4] www.chron.com/news/houston-texas/houston/article/Woodlands-teenagers-go-on-shower-strike-for-full-4389591.php

money for a nonprofit called Well Aware.[5] Ever heard of it?" asked Kurt.

The two assistants shook their heads. "Nope. Not me," Neal confessed.

Raj shrugged. "Me neither."

"Well Aware provides clean water to orphanages, schools and hospitals in Kenya," Kurt continued. "The girls in The Woodlands figured out the amount of water they ran to take one five-minute shower was more water than the average person in a Third World slum has access to for an entire day.

"He also said the girls found out a child in Africa dies every 20 seconds because their family has no access to clean water … and this shower strike was something teens could do to make a difference," Kurt concluded.

"That's pretty awesome," Neal agreed.

"But, the shower strike wasn't just for teens," Kurt commented. "He said there were CEOs, unions, entire offices and college campuses participating … and when the kids at their school asked The Woodlands girls how they could go without showering, the volleyball team's answer was pretty direct. They told them, 'We're saving lives!'"[6]

✦ ✦ ✦ ✦ ✦

By the next afternoon, the teleconferences with regional operations management had been scheduled. Prior to those, Kurt scheduled three additional teleconferences with supervisory-level personnel. He wanted to speak with these hands-on men and women in order to get

[5] www.wellawareworld.org/
[6] www.chron.com/news/houston-texas/houston/article/Woodlands-teenagers-go-on-shower-strike-for-full-4389591.php

their reactions and input, which he knew would be straightforward responses.

"I'll open by explaining the meaning of the word, 'culture,' Kurt began. "We want our employees to know culture not only means the various countries represented in our international workforce but the behaviors and beliefs of our company that are passed down from one generation of employees to another. Then, secondly, we need to communicate that environmental stewardship is something we incorporate into every moment of our lives, 24/7, not just something we do while we're at work."[7]

"That's what I've picked up from Jim Corley," Raj added. "He's been a great role-model, and while some may call people who want to preserve the environment 'tree huggers,' Mr. Corley seems to make every day of his life an opportunity to take care of our planet."

"So, how do we get there from here?" Neal wanted to know.

"Well, just like in our effort to encourage a safety culture several years ago, feedback is essential."

Neal looked puzzled. "Feedback?"

"It's a tool our teammates use to remind us about any time our behavior impacts the environment," said Kurt.

"Like when someone reminds you that plastic water bottles can fill up a landfill?" Neal asked.

"Or when we in this country don't think about how much water we're using when we take showers?" added Raj.

[7] *Safety 24/7*, Anderson and Lorber.

Kurt smiled. "Both great examples, guys."

✦ ✦ ✦ ✦ ✦

That evening, as Kurt walked down the hall to visit Janet in the hospital's ICU, he was unexpectedly aware of the sounds and odors around him. As he waited for his wife, Jessica, to come back from visiting her mother, he looked around the pristine waiting room, which had just been cleaned in preparation for the evening's visitors.

The doors to the ICU opened and he looked up, expecting to see his wife. Instead, a nurse dressed in blue scrubs appeared. When she saw him, she walked over. "May I get you anything?" she asked.

"Oh no, I'm fine … just waiting for my wife."

The nurse smiled in recognition. "You must be Jessica's husband."

"Yes," he replied. "I'm Kurt Bradshaw."

"Your mother-in-law is making slow but steady progress," she said.

"That is certainly great to hear." Kurt cleared his throat. "I know this may be a bit off the subject, but I've been impressed by your hospital's 'green' policies, like the water conservation reminders in the public restrooms and the recycling bins in the parking lot. Can you tell me more about the program?"

The nurse smiled again. "It's been a team effort," she began. "I have a few minutes if you'd like to hear how it all began."

"Please go on," Kurt nodded.

"We've come a long way since our environmentally friendly protocols have been put in place," she offered. "But, what really got my attention

– were three things shared during a hospital staff meeting. First of all, they began the meeting with a quote from Florence Nightingale, the founder of nursing. We have it posted near the nurses' station … and remember, this was during the 19th century. Anyway, Florence said, 'No amount of medical knowledge will lessen the accountability of nurses to do, that is, manage the environment to promote positive life processes.'"[8]

"Wow! She was definitely ahead of her time," exclaimed Kurt.

"She recognized the importance of a healthy environment when it came to patients,"[9] the nurse continued, "and during that same meeting, the hospital's environmental health officer also told us about a report from the World Health Organization that found close to one-fourth of the diseases experienced by the world's population can be attributed to environmental exposures."

"Like Janet?"

She nodded. "That statistic is hitting close to home for you, isn't it?"

Kurt shook his head. "I can't believe how close."

"The other information that kick-started my interest in helping this hospital 'go green,' as they say, is the healthcare industry in the U.S. produces more than 2.4 million tons of waste – about 30 pounds per patient bed per day – while also being one of the largest energy consumers in most communities,"[10] the nurse continued.

Kurt was definitely interested so he encouraged the nurse to continue by asking exactly what "going green" meant to the hospital.

[8] www.neefusa.org/pdf/NursingBooklet.pdf
[9] www.uab.edu/reynolds/nightingale/life
[10] http://honors.usf.edu/documents/thesis/u91904693.pdf

"It's all about behaviors or activities that improve environmental outcomes, at least that's how our program is structured," she explained. "One of a nurse's most important skills is the ability to assess our patients. That same skill also can be used to reduce waste and conserve energy and resources."

"So what is your definition for 'conservation'?" Kurt asked.

"Much the same as everyone else's," she said. "We look for ways to reduce, reuse, recycle and restore."

Kurt nodded. "So do you know how much you're saving from a dollar standpoint?"

"You mean aside from creating a better, healthier environment for our patients and being a better institutional citizen in our community?"

Kurt flushed with embarrassment. "Er, uh, well, yes, even though the other reasons you named are very important."

The nurse smiled. "I understand saving money is important as well, particularly to our administrators responsible for the bottom line ... and I'd say we've kept them happy as well as we've moved into a 'green' and environmentally friendly workplace. Our sustainability program saved the hospital $236,000 in 2010, $309,000 in 2011 and $308,000 just in the first half of 2012.[11]

"I'm impressed," Kurt said. The nurse glanced at her watch again. "I could talk for hours about environmentalism," she said, "but to better answer your question, a speaker from the Environmental Protection Agency said for every dollar saved through energy conservation, an additional $20 in new revenue is gained.[12] Our CEO said by simply

[11] www.forbes.com/sites/davidferris/2012/07/31/how-a-boston-hospital-saves-money-by-going-green/
[12] www.energystar.gov/ia/partners/spp_res/LFES_Healthcare.pdf

turning off lights we weren't using, switching to LED lighting and small, common sense habits, we had already boosted our net operating income by 10 percent – and we're just getting started," she added.

"Thanks for sharing," Kurt said, standing to shake the nurse's hand, "and for taking such good care of Janet."

The woman smiled and turned to leave. "It's my job, taking care of our patients," she said, "just like it's our job – yours and mine – to take care of our planet."

Snapshot

Definitions

1. **E. coli** – *E. coli* is the name of a germ, or bacterium, that lives in the digestive tracts of humans and animals and is transmitted to humans through contaminated urban runoff into lakes and rivers, raw milk, raw produce and poorly processed meats.
2. **Healthier Hospital Initiative** – (HHI) is a national campaign to implement a completely new approach to improving environmental health and sustainability in the healthcare sector.
3. **Sustainability** – Based on a simple principle: Everything that we need for our survival and well-being depends, either directly or indirectly, on our natural environment. Sustainability creates and maintains the conditions under which humans and nature can exist in productive harmony, fulfilling the social, economic and other requirements of present and future generations. It is important to assure we have and will continue to have the water, materials, and resources to protect human health and our environment.
4. **Staph** – Staphylococcus bacteria, a type of germ commonly found on the skin or in the nose of even healthy individuals, causes infections. Most cause no problems other than minor skin reactions but can become deadly if the bacteria invade deeper into the body, entering the bloodstream, joints, bones, lungs or heart.
5. **The global village** – Philosopher Marshall McLuhan described how the globe has been contracted into a village by electric technology and the instantaneous movement of

information from every quarter to every point at the same time. In bringing all social and political functions together in a sudden implosion, electric speed heightened human awareness of responsibility to an intense degree.

6. **Urban runoff** – Surface runoff of rainwater created by urbanization, which is a major source of water pollution in urban communities worldwide.

Steps Toward Stewardship

1. Environmental stewardship begins with you, me and everyone else in our home, neighborhood, workplace, school, community, state and nation.
2. Our planet is home for all of us, and if we all remain aware of its importance, we'll be making a good first step.
3. When it comes to environmental stewardship, we must all be on the same team – and that includes collaborating and sharing with our competitors when it comes to sustainability.
4. A company's culture not only means the various countries represented in the workforce but also the behaviors and beliefs of the company that are passed down from one generation of employees to another.
5. Environmental stewardship is something we incorporate into every moment of our lives, 24/7, not just something we do while we're at work.
6. Feedback is a powerful tool that's essential in reminding us at any time of how our behavior impacts the environment.

ADDITIONAL ACTIVITIES

1. Pick a company at random from anywhere in the world and try to find evidence of an attempt at environmental stewardship, including any cost savings cited.
2. It is estimated that hospitals generate 30 pounds or more of waste per patient bed per day. Select five hospitals. For each hospital, calculate the amount of waste generated per year by each of the five hospitals.
3. Urban runoff can be a deadly contaminate to coastal waters after rainfall. Find newspaper articles about individuals who have fallen victim to this contaminate. Discuss whether warning signs or other types of signals were available.
4. Using a diary for one week, write down all of the ways in which you show a commitment to environmental stewardship. This could include anything, from using environmentally friendly products to reducing use of certain resources to recycling or using recycled products.
5. Go to the Well Aware website and discuss at least three projects that this organization is currently working on or will be working on. What is the value of this and similar organizations?

Jump-starting the Momentum of Awareness

Kurt slept fitfully in his wife's absence. He found himself working past midnight and then, totally exhausted, falling into bed, only to toss and turn in his sleep until he shook himself awake the next morning.

Tonight was no different, except for his dream, one of helpless, hopeless carnage.

A savage environmental disaster had destroyed life as they knew it. He and Jessica were huddled together under their makeshift shelter as they watched, helplessly, as their daughter, Shannon, slipped from their grasp and was whisked away on a small piece of the ravaged landscape. "Hold on, baby," her mother called as the young girl disappeared over the horizon. "We'll get you back safely. Just hold on!"

In the aftermath of the disaster, food and water had all but disappeared. Nothing would grow in the polluted earth and there was no fuel to keep them warm. All comforts, as they had known, were gone … all due to decades of the Earth's inhabitants squandering resources and selfishly abusing the environment.

His throat was parched and his insides ached from eating the remaining insects and weeds … whatever they could forage. "Jess … Jess," he called out in the blackness of the early morning.

Kurt awoke from the nightmare, soaked with perspiration. It took a few moments for him to recognize his surroundings, and he breathed a prayer of thanks when he found himself in his bedroom and not clinging to a defoliated, scorched piece of earth.

As had been his routine, Kurt arrived at the hospital about 5:30 a.m., bringing Jessica a Thermos of coffee, fruit and some of their neighbor's homemade bread. Once she had eaten, Jessica showered in her mother's hospital bathroom.

Jessica's mother had been moved from ICU but was still being sedated while IV antibiotics continued to battle the infections.

Kurt sat by her bed, reading the morning paper.

The woman stirred. "Loggerheads."

"Janet, can I get you something? Some water?" Kurt asked, not knowing what else to say.

"Stop killing … Loggerheads," she mumbled and then drifted back into a deep sleep.

"She still sleeping?" Jessica pushed open the bathroom door and walked to her mother's bedside, stopping to kiss her husband. "I'm the cleanest person in this room," she announced teasingly as she towel-dried her hair.

Kurt whistled his quiet appreciation of his attractive wife. "You smell amazing!" he said. "Just one question: What are 'Loggerheads?' Your mother seemed to be trying to save them."

Jessica smoothed a strand of her mother's hair. "I think she was talking about a breed of turtles that are just about extinct."

"Dying off on their own or are they being killed?"

"From what mother's friends were saying when they visited yesterday, 1,000 or so of these turtles were getting caught and accidentally killed each year in fishermen's nets off the coast of Mexico," Jessica explained. "The 'girls' were encouraging mother to get well so they can all do something to save the Loggerheads."

Kurt smiled. "It'll give Janet something to look forward to when she gets well," he said as he embraced his wife and kissed her before grabbing his backpack. "Have to get to work," he said, "Oh, and by the way, we've got to stop meeting like this," he teased.

Arriving at the office, Kurt stopped by the break room to refill his coffee mug. He was soon joined by Ron Kaiser, one of the company's continual resisters when it came to any type of change. Kurt shook the man's outstretched hand. "Hello, Kaiser," he said.

"How are you this morning, my friend?" Kaiser responded, more amiably than usual. "Hey, I'm glad I caught you this morning."

Before Kurt could answer Kaiser's question, the man continued. "I understand young Neal Jacobson is headed to Texas to hold some kind of environmental safety seminar or something like that."

"Environmental stewardship feedback session," Kurt corrected.

"Anyway, I asked his uncle if I could go, too, just to make sure everything goes all right. Jacobson Sr. gave me his okay. Mind if I tag along?"

Kurt had never trusted Kaiser. Something about his arrogant approach. "Well, thanks for letting me know," said Kurt, trying to remain civil. "Might just learn something as well."

"I knew you would see the benefit," Kaiser smiled. "I'll make my reservations. I look forward to also getting to know Junior a little better."

"I think he prefers to be called Neal," said Kurt.

"Okay, whatever. I'll call him anything he wants me to if it will make him happy."

Walking to his office, Kurt shook his head, disgusted. Kaiser had moved up rapidly in the company, playing similar political games, worming – no, snaking – his way from one level to the next. His plan to get closer to Neal Jacobson was just another example.

Preparing for the morning's teleconference, Kurt felt comfortable with is agenda. He joined Raj and Neal in the company's media room … and because he had launched the company's safety culture with some of the same supervisors, Kurt knew the teleconference would go fairly smoothly.

As the IT professionals began bringing the teleconference centers around the world online, Kurt looked over his notes. "Don't be surprised if there's a little pushback," he told the two men sitting by his side. "There always is, but sooner or later, we get them onboard."

"Sounds easy enough," Raj said.

"Sure, just like riding a bull ..." thought Kurt. The IT coordinator signaled for Kurt to begin.

"Good morning, afternoon or evening, ladies and gentleman, as the case may be in your time zone. I appreciate your attendance. Now for the housekeeping. As most of you who have teleconferenced before know, we may have a few seconds – or more – delay between our responses, so just bear with me and we'll try to make this brief. I know some of you really want to get back to work, right?"

The group on the split screens laughed.

"I believe everyone knows, or has previously spoken with Raj and Neal," Kurt began. "So I would like to take this opportunity to introduce Martin Avery, one of the newer members of our management team. Martin has an exceptional background in transformational change, but I'll let him tell you more about it later during the call.

"As most everyone is aware, thanks to your outstanding efforts, we successfully elevated safety from a priority to a core value within our company. Now we want to make that same transformation when it comes to environmental stewardship."

"Here, here," came a voice from a distant land.

"It's about time," said another.

"I appreciate your enthusiasm," Kurt replied, although he knew not everyone on the call likely felt the same way. "As many of you know, our operations have the potential to significantly impact our environment, and if we keep doing things the same way we have always done them, then we are not only responsible for the shape our planet is in when we pass it along to our children and the next generation after that, but we, as a company, also increase our exposure to risks – costly risks.

"Some of you may have read recently that one of our competitors received a hefty fine as well as some pretty damaging publicity, not to mention all the cleanup they are having to do, so nobody knows what their final bill is going to be."

A supervisor from one of the operations in Africa spoke up. "I don't think we have a choice – about environmental stewardship – do we?" he asked in a deep, heavily accented voice. "We are watching our country, literally, go from one shortage of resources to another, and with more international industries coming here, we must do something. We cannot sit by and simply watch what happens."[1]

"My point exactly," Kurt said, "plus, as I mentioned, we have seen our competitors pay a high price, literally, for manmade environmental disasters. Mr. Jacobson's vision is to make environmental stewardship a core value, so let's begin by looking at what we all learned about moving safety from our heads to our hearts.

"It is the same with environmental stewardship," he continued. "When we're committed to living an environmentally friendly life, these habits follow us from work to home to hobbies and recreation. It's every aspect of our lives, 24/7."

"I have a question," another supervisor chimed in. "Do we use the same approach to the environment as we do with safety?"

"Absolutely," Kurt replied. "And, like safety, when we as a company make taking care of the environment a core value, we not only attract good people, but we also save money and build better ties to the community."

"Okay, okay, I get it," came a gruff, Australian-accented voice. "But what's in it for me, mate?"

[1] www.thedti.gov.za/industrial_development/industrial_development.jsp

"Good question," Kurt responded. "So how did you fare during last summer's drought?"[2]

"We call it 'big dry,' and we didn't like it at all," the man responded immediately. "Farmers took the brunt, but it impacted all of us. Produce prices went sky high. So did beef prices. Definitely made a difference at our table."

"And the problem was due to …?" asked Kurt.

"Climate change, I guess, and all of the problems that come along with it," said the supervisor.

"So, what if our company served as a role model for energy efficiency by cutting back on our use of electricity, or generating our own through wind and solar and by investing in hybrid or natural gas-powered vehicles?"

"I still don't see what's in it for me," the Australian supervisor snorted.

"Let me put it another way," Kurt continued patiently. "In just about every country in the world, energy efficiency is seen as the biggest and best option for reducing greenhouse gas emissions and rising power bills.[3] Australia came in dead last in 2010 during an energy efficiency survey, so if things continue as they have been, your climate will continue to get hotter and your droughts even longer and more severe.[4]

"Furthermore, in other countries, businesses and households are making money while they cut emissions. They are going to be winners in the green revolution through energy efficiency and innovation," he concluded.

---

[2] www.businessday.com.au/business/markets/big-dry-sends-global-milk-prices-soaring-20130320-2gffb.html
[3] www.thegef.org/gef/node/4081
[4] https://theconversation.com/australia-ignores-energy-efficiency-burns-money-12

"... and if we all cut emissions and use energy more efficiently, that means more money in my pocket?" the supervisor wondered aloud.

"Exactly," said Kurt. "I think you're beginning to see the bigger picture."

"But, what about our coal industry? We have several countries, including China, lining up to mine and export it," the man continued with his questions. "Besides that, we use a lot of coal in Australia."

"So, if coal is mined in Australia, does that mean you have to use it inefficiently? Or, use it at all for that matter?" Kurt said, putting the proverbial ball back in the supervisor's court.

"Well, if you put it in those terms," the man began.

Kurt smiled as he interrupted. "Since you mentioned our friends in China, let's take Beijing as an example."

The supervisor from China spoke up. "Oh, I see you've heard about our air problem?"

"I think everyone has," said another supervisor.

"When did I lose control of this meeting?" Kurt joked. "But seriously, there are many places in China where air quality has suffered. Coal-generated electricity, as well as more vehicles burning fossil fuels, are good starting points in finding the cause. Can you tell us more, Mr. Zhang?"

"You are right," he said in somber tones. "In Beijing, many children can no longer play outdoors. They must play in special domed structures with air filtration equipment. In poorer areas, many suffer from asthma.[5]

There was also a study just released by the American National

[5] www.beijing-kids.com/magazine/2012/03/22/Asthma-Woes

Academy of Science that projects the widespread use of coal in northern China will result in 500 million Chinese losing 2.5 billion years of life expectancy due to outdoor air pollution.[6]

"That's unbelievable!" Neal exclaimed. "So, how has the air quality impacted business?"

"Some people, mainly expatriates, are leaving because the air is bad, so there is definitely a drain on talent," Zhang continued, "and I have lost some of our best employees because of the pollution. At the same time, new employees are negotiating for hardship pay since the air quality is so bad.[7] I think you could say we are in survival mode at present," he added in careful English.

"Is your government stepping in to clean up this pollution?" asked a supervisor from Indonesia.

"Because of past incidents, people in Beijing no longer trust the pollution counts the government reports. They think the government is hiding how bad our air really is,"[8] Zhang said, shaking his head, "and because of various plant and automobile emissions, I have heard this pollution problem is expected to continue through 2025."

"I think pollution is a problem in many areas of the world," Allison Catewell of the UK spoke up, "and whether you're an innocent bystander and the stuff is just blowing into your country or you're guilty of generating even more pollution, we're all having problems."

"Hear, hear! My sentiments exactly. Stop blowing your junk into our clean air," called out Evan Smythe, a veteran supervisor also from the UK.

---

[6] Houston Chronicle, July 9, 2013

[7] www.nytimes.com/2013/04/23/world/asia/pollution-is-radically-changing-childhood-in-chinas-cities.html?pagewanted=all&_r=0

[8] www.nytimes.com/2013/04/23/world/asia/pollution-is-radically-changing-childhood-in-chinas-cities.html?pagewanted=all&_r=0

"Recently in London, *The Guardian* reported many of the city's pollution monitors recorded "high" nitrogen dioxide levels coming from fumes and microscopic particles," Allison continued. "As I understood, the smog was made up of acids, chemicals, metals and dust – you name it – drifting across from the continent and mixing with London's diesel exhaust, all trapped in the still air.[9] Bloody awful. That's what it is," she said.

"I didn't realize it was that bad," Kurt empathized.

At this point, a familiar voice from one of the company's South American projects spoke up. "If having clean air and clean water means something to any of you, the only way we can continue working and living is what Kurt here is proposing … being more careful with the environment."

"John Sullivan, is that you?" Kurt spoke up. "Didn't know you'd have time to sit in."

"It's important to what we're all doing over here. With all the mining you guys in China and many others are doing – around the globe, but particularly in Australia these days – I don't want to find m'self wearing a gas mask one of these days. Nothing against coal-fired plants, mind you. We do have a lot of coal mining going on in Australia, but our environmental policy Down Under isn't bending for anybody … even the Shenhua Group from China, who say we've changed the regulations on them since they started their big Watermark project five years ago,"[10] Sullivan continued.

"What changes?" a supervisor from the U.S. wanted to know.

[9] www.guardian.co.uk/environment/2013/mar/19/uk-air-pollution-health-crisis
[10] www.smh.com.au/business/china-mine-boss-vents-concerns-20130423-2icvj.html

"Well, for one, we've instituted mining and carbon taxes, which only add to China's recovery costs for the coal," said Sullivan. "The Chinese are unhappy because their country uses a huge amount of coal each year and some of Australia's business community want policies changed to encourage more Chinese investment."

"It's always about the money," a representative from Japan observed aloud.

"Which is why we want to make taking care of the environment a core value at every one of our sites around the world," Kurt pointed out. "Whether you like it or not, it is a matter of survival ... for our business, our families and the health of our planet."

Hans Larsen, another of the company's veteran supervisors, spoke next. "All I know is, air pollution is being regularly reported on the TV here in Norway,[11] and my mother has developed breathing problems because of the muck in the air, all because of cars on our roads and more wood burners across the country. My mother – poor thing, she doesn't even own a car!"

Kurt had a ready response. "So, Mr. Larsen, let's say you see someone driving into the company's parking lot with smoke pouring from their exhaust pipe. What kind of conversation would you have?"

"You mean after I had taken an iron bar to the car?" Larsen responded, half-jokingly.

"No, no, let's take the iron bar out of the scene and go through what we call an Environmental Conversation Opportunity, or ECO. Do you recall the steps we use for the Safety 24/7 Conversation?"

[11] www.environment.no/Topics/Air-pollution/Local-air-pollution/

"Sure," the supervisor responded. "We use it all the time."

"That's great. So let's go through the process together, just as a reminder," Kurt suggested as he projected a list of the five steps from an environmental perspective:

> **Step 1: *Observe*** means training ourselves to be more aware of people's behaviors ... both what they are doing to show proper environmental stewardship and what they might be doing that puts the environment at risk.
>
> **Step 2**: ***Accentuate*** the positive to lower the person's natural defensiveness, as well as reinforce those environmentally sensitive behaviors we want him to keep doing.
>
> **Step 3: *Explore*** allows the person to figure out what he did, either taking the environment into consideration or not doing so, which helps him begin to take *ownership* of his behavior.
>
> **Step 4: *Emphasize*** the consequences of the person's actions to help him understand the impact his behavior could have on the environment.
>
> **Step 5: *Agree*** on future actions, which confirms the person understands he is accountable for his behavior and responsible for the impact he has on the environment.

"Okay, that all makes sense," agreed Larsen, "and I like how easily the Safety 24/7 Conversation steps can be converted into an Environmental Conversation Opportunity. Makes it really easy to remember. But getting back to the smoking car, what kind of positive reinforcement could I give that driver?"

"What behavior did you see that you would want him to continue?" prodded Kurt.

"Well … he was one of the few people I've actually seen driving slowly through the parking lot. So can I Accentuate his safe behavior and then continue with the ECO?" the Norwegian wanted to know.

"Absolutely! And, we want you, our frontline leaders, to make taking care of our planet a habit so you can model the ECO and actual environmentally beneficial behaviors for your employees as well as others," Kurt said, "So, we've come up with the following diagram to help everyone," he added as he clicked to the next page of his presentation. "After we've gone over it, I'd like to hear some feedback."

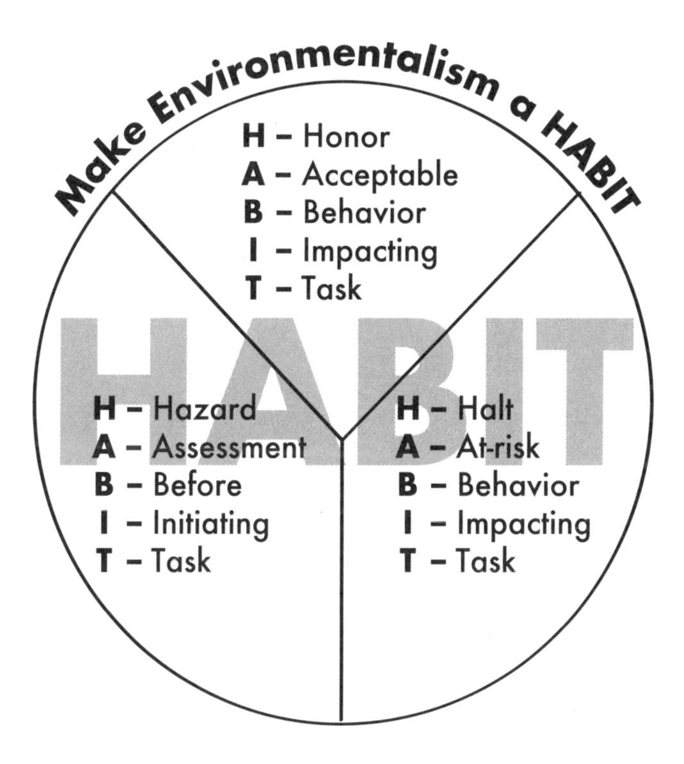

"We 'Honor' the positive behaviors we observe," Kurt explained. "We conduct an environmental 'Hazard Assessment' before beginning a task, and we use the Environmental Conversation Opportunity to halt a task if we see an at-risk behavior that could hurt the environment.

"In other words, we Make Environmentalism a HABIT," Kurt emphasized, "and just as you have been safety role models, from this point on you are environmental role models for the men and women you supervise.

"We want this company to be the industry leader when it comes to leaving our environment in better shape than we found it at every job site as well as in our office environments," he finished to applause and words of encouragement from the supervisors. "So what about feedback?"

Larsen was the first to speak. "It's easy enough. I say, let's give it a try. See what happens. Couldn't hurt."

"Same here," Allison Catewell said. "Certainly can't hurt. I mean, some Londoners are moving to the countryside, looking for clean air. My cousin and her family moved to Guernsey, an island in the English Channel, just to avoid raising her family in the city's pollution."

"Me too, mate," Sullivan said. "It's either try to remedy this problem or sit and watch as our planet becomes sicker. I'll start making it a habit today. Tomorrow's not soon enough."

"Speaking of tomorrow, we'll meet back here for Part II of our conference – same time, same place," Kurt said, "and your assignment is to follow John Sullivan's suggestion and begin making environmental stewardship a HABIT today."

Snapshot

Definitions

1. Five Steps of the Environmental Conversation Opportunity

   Step 1: *Observe* – Training ourselves to be more aware of people's behaviors … both what they are doing to show environmental stewardship and what they might be doing that puts the environment at risk.

   Step 2: *Accentuate* – Accentuate the positive to lower the person's natural defensiveness, as well as reinforce those environmentally sensitive behaviors we want him to keep doing.

   Step 3: *Explore* – Allow the person to figure out what he did, either taking the environment into consideration or not doing so, which helps him begin to take ownership of his behavior.

   Step 4: *Emphasize* – Highlight the consequences of the person's actions to help him understand the impact his behavior could have on the environment.

   Step 5: *Agree* – Agree on future actions, which confirms the person understands he is accountable for his behavior and responsible for the impact he has on the environment.

2. **Employee buy-in** – Aligning employees with their company's mission and core values by helping them understand how their day-to-day work impacts the larger mission of the company, providing the support they need – such as timely communication, linking training to overall strategy and by appreciating their efforts to achieve the vision, rewarding them with monetary as well as non-monetary recognition.

3. **Environmental Role Models** – Those who choose to adopt and make environmental stewardship a 24/7 lifestyle, wherever they are – home, work, the community or traveling around the world. Their behavior reflects their environmentally friendly lifestyle and they serve as role models as they encourage others to become environmental stewards.

4. **The Environmental Stewardship HABIT** – See diagram on page 173.

STEPS TOWARD STEWARDSHIP

1. Be open to change. Expect some people to be slower to accept change, but align yourself with early adopters and then focus on the late adopters, demonstrating the progress being made toward fulfilling the vision.

2. Be willing to speak up, advocate and have ECOs.

3. Research the various aspects of environmental stewardship and be ready to present the upside as your company moves toward more active, corporate-wide HABITS.

4. Never fail to celebrate progress, from bottom-line savings to creating smaller environmental footprints or bringing more "adopters" onboard.

ADDITIONAL ACTIVITIES

1. The U.S. Environmental Protection Agency has set National Ambient Air Quality Standards (NAAQS) for six principal pollutants, which are called "criteria" pollutants. What are these six principal pollutants and what are the standards, as in parts per million (ppm) by volume, parts per billion (ppb) by volume, and micrograms per cubic meter of air (µg/m3)?

2. After researching, write a 500-word discussion of the primary environmental problems in the two countries of your choosing. Include any current mitigation efforts being conducted in both countries. Are they succeeding? If not, why not?
3. This book has discussed the NIMBY mindset in previous chapters. Why or why not is this mindset a danger to environmental stewardship?
4. Visit a nearby construction site and identify at least two observable environmental hazards. On paper, describe these hazards and then describe how you would handle an ECO. Write out the dialogue between you, as a co-worker, and another employee.
5. Using the Make Environmental Stewardship a HABIT diagram, dissect each of the three sections and explain each step within that section. At the conclusion of your explanation, decide which part you consider essential in resolving a behavioral issue when it comes to protecting the environment.

Environmental Tips: Things You Can Do

Inflate Your Tires
Keeping your tires adequately inflated can save you $840 per year and keep 250 lbs. of carbon dioxide out of the air! Check them monthly to be sure.

Change Your Car's Air Filter
Check your car's air filter once a month. You can save $130 per year and keep 100 lbs. of CO_2 from entering our atmosphere.

Install a Low-flow Showerhead
Using less water in the shower not only conserves this precious resource, but it also means less energy is used to heat the water, saving 350 lbs. of carbon dioxide and $150.

Buy Products Locally
Think about how much oil it takes to get a bottle of water to you from Fiji.

Buy Minimally Packaged Goods
Less packaging reduces garbage by up to 30 percent. You can also save 1,200 lbs. of carbon dioxide and $1,000 per year.

Source: www.DoSomething.org

9 From Vision to Core Value

After assembling his team in the teleconference facility the following day, Kurt stood in front of the microphone awaiting the tele-technician's cue to begin the second part of his presentation. "Once again, good morning, afternoon or evening, ladies and gentlemen," he began. "As you may have noticed, I make a HABIT of beginning these meetings on time, and I promise to continue the HABIT of ending on time, which I think are both good HABITs to have."

Amid the audience's laughter, the supervisor from South America shouted. "Let me guess, the keyword is *HABIT*," he announced. "Do I win the prize?"

"I'm glad you're paying attention, Fabio," Kurt chuckled. "As for your prize, you get to take me to dinner the next time I'm in town."

Kurt waited for the laughter to die down before continuing. "But seriously, folks, we've got some important work to do today. One of the most difficult tasks in the business world is implementing change."

"My people hate change," Allison Catewell confirmed.

"Here too," said Mr. Zhang. "Until we got the buy-in from our employees to build a culture of safety, it was as difficult as – how do you say it in the U.S.? – finding a needle in a haystack."

"Good comparison, Mr. Zhang," Kurt said, "so that's why I'd like to reintroduce Martin Avery. He brings with him an impressive management background, which will be evident as we move into the next part of today's business. Martin's going to show us how to successfully lead the change process."

"No pressure, to be sure," Evan Smythe said wryly.

"Hello, and thank you all for participating in today's call," Avery began. "Environmental stewardship is no longer a choice." "It's now a mandate, and because the stakes are so high, we're going to rely on an eight-step approach developed by John Kotter, a Harvard professor and author who now heads Kotter International, a consulting firm known for its expertise all over the world."

Sounding confident, the young man continued. "I had the distinct opportunity of studying with Dr. Kotter while I was a graduate student at Harvard. In fact, he was one of my favorite professors.

"One of the things Dr. Kotter is best known for is his eight-step transformational process which, you'll be happy to know, the first three steps have been completed, thanks to our CEO's vision and passionate belief that this change must become a core value for this company.

"I made a list of Dr. Kotter's Eight Steps,"[1] Martin explained to the group as he stood and walked to an easel. "I hope all of you can read my writing:"

[1] http://www.kotterinternational.com/our-principles/changesteps/changesteps

✦ **Step 1: Establish a Sense of Urgency**
Help others see the need for change and feel a gut-level determination to move and win, *now*.

✦ **Step 2: Create the Guiding Coalition**
Assemble a group and give them enough power to lead the change.

✦ **Step 3: Develop a Change Vision**
Create a vision to direct the change effort, and develop strategies to achieve that vision. Tell all stakeholders how the future will be different from the past.

Martin then turned the page to reveal Step Four.

"This is where you folks will begin:"

✦ **Step 4: Communicating the Vision for Buy-in**
Make sure as many people as possible understand and accept the vision and the strategy.

"This is where we are today," Avery said. "We want you, as part of our guiding coalition, to see the urgency of Mr. Jacobson's vision of making environmental stewardship a core value of this company and then communicating it to your employees."

"I'm sitting here, listening, and then wondering if you might be able to provide some tips on how we actually bring our people onboard?" asked a project manager from Abu Dhabi.

"Excellent question!" Kurt encouraged. "Martin, would you show us how?'"

"Sure … and to answer the question, when we share Mr. Jacobson's vision of environmentalism, we must (1) Keep it simple, and (2) Keep it vivid if you want people to buy into it."

"That will be easy for me." A supervisor from Mexico spoke up. "In my country, there is an ongoing battle for water, particularly the Encinillas Valley. Some farmers are ready to go to war over water, if you can imagine. Because there is a shortage, anything we can do to reduce our use of water is a plus… for everyone."[2]

"That's a perfect example," Martin pointed out. "A real example is of much greater value than just reading a company policy. So link the story to the vision. Our ideas to reduce, reuse, recycle and restore should be understandable by anyone of any age."

He stopped to take a sip of water. "I'm going to show you two versions of how to communicate our vision – and the importance of making it simple, clear and to the point.[3]"

As Martin spoke, the IT specialist projected the following for everyone to see on their laptops:

> **Version One:** Our goal is to reduce our environmental impact at each worksite and facility so that our ecological footprint becomes perceptually lower than all our major competitors, worldwide. Similarly, we are now targeting new project development lifecycles, process times and other environmentally relevant activities for change.
>
> **Version Two:** We are going to become more environmentally responsible and accountable than anyone in our industry.

[2] http://fnsnews.nmsu.edu/page/3/ - "Water Fights Flare," May 7, 2013
[3] www.kotterinternational.com/our-principles/changesteps/changesteps

He turned to face the participants. "Ladies and gentlemen, I ask you – which version will be more effective with your teams?"

"Number two," came the response.

"Exactly," Martin smiled. "So, it will be your responsibility to help your teams understand and believe in Mr. Jacobson's vision. Be a role model, encourage your team members to find ways to reduce, reuse, recycle and restore our environment … and let them know, the time is now!" Martin finished, barely able to hide his enthusiasm.

"Thank you, Martin. We're off to a good start," Kurt applauded, very impressed at how much the new manager had energized the people on the teleconference. "Now you know why we hired him," Kurt said to the group, "and before we end today's conversation, there are just a few more things I'd like you to remember.

"But first, a question: If I asked you to stop a project, right in the middle of things, because I saw something that wasn't good for the environment, would you trust me enough to do that?"

"Thanks to *Safety 24/7*,[4] I do think we have built a culture of trust, at least with our older employees," said Smythe, the British manager. "It's the newer ones who worry me most."

"How many of you remember the requirements for building trust?" asked Kurt, standing at the white board.

"I got that one," Hank O'Leary offered confidently. Hank was a relative old-timer with the company.

Picking up a marker, Kurt invited Hank to talk while he wrote.

[4] See www.safety247.org

"First of all, you have to know that people don't all see things the same way," Hank began, "and, in some cases, both of you may be right."

Kurt paused. "Good start, Hank. What's next?"

"Listen and be receptive because you may not know it all."

"Good. Ready for number three," Kurt said.

Hank rubbed his bearded chin. "Hmmm. I guess, you need to ask questions, letting the person know you're listening and are interested. And the next one is to focus on the areas you agree on."

Kurt struggled to keep up. "Okay, ready for the next," he said finally.

"Then you need to act on the feedback you get," Hank said, "and the last is: Be sure to follow up."

Kurt put down the marker and took his seat. "Let's give Hank a round of applause for his reminder," he said, "… because without trust, we're in a boat without a rudder."

He waited for the applause before making his next point. "We want to approach stewardship for the environment as a core value … and in making this change, we want to give our people a chance to succeed, wherever they are, at whatever level of understanding … so, how do we achieve this?"

Maurice Godet of the office in Paris spoke up: "We praise our people immediately," he said, "and, believe me, I know that works. I've seen it, not just in their eyes but also in the hearts of my people.

"Next, you are very specific about what they've done right," Godet continued in his heavy French accent. "And you share your positive feelings. I must tell you, I was honestly excited, seeing our people make Safety 24/7 Conversations and safety awareness their personal habits. Oh, and there's a third point – you encourage them to keep going, even beyond what they are already doing right."

"Excellent, Maurice!" praised Kurt.

Martin Avery continued the conversation by revealing author John Kotter's final four steps for making transformational change:

- **Step 5: Empower broad-based action by removing barriers for change and through honest dialogue.**
- **Step 6: Facilitate short-term wins by creating visible success as soon as possible.**
- **Step 7: Don't let up and don't give up.** Resistance to change is normal, but if you're successful, some of the signs will be:
  - More projects being added.
  - Senior leadership focused on clarifying the vision and purpose.
  - Employees empowered at all levels to lead projects.
  - Reduced interdependencies between areas.
  - Constant effort to keep urgency high.
  - Consistent show of proof that the new way is working.
- **Step 8: Incorporating change into corporate culture by:**
  - Proving the new way is better.
  - Continuing to communicate success.
  - Emphasizing new practices with incentives and rewards.
  - Reinforcing the culture with every new employee.[5]

[5] www.kotterinternational.com/our-principles/changesteps/changesteps

"I think these are all fairly self-explanatory, but if you have questions, I invite your emails," said Martin, "and remember, there are no such things as stupid questions."

"I do have one question," Mr. Zhang said. "Exactly what is 'transformational change'?"

"I'm sorry I neglected to explain that," Martin apologized. "Transformational, or transformative, change is a shift in a company's business culture, resulting from a change in the underlying strategy and processes that the organization has used in the past. A transformational change is designed to be organization-wide and is enacted over a period of time.[6]

"Any more questions?" asked the younger man.

There was a round of appreciative applause.

Kurt was next at the microphone. "I must tell you, ladies and gentlemen, I'm very impressed with your enthusiasm. I've also seen the results of what you're doing from a safety perspective. And, I must tell you, if we can achieve the same level of environmental responsibility, we will be helping to ensure our species is around as long as the Earth keeps rotating on its axis."

As he scanned the faces projected on the screens in front of him, Kurt saw some puzzled looks.

"What I mean," he clarified, "is that if we can keep reducing, reusing, recycling and restoring – not just whenever there's a recycling drive – but making these four activities personal habits. If we begin taking care of our natural resources – our water, land and air (not just during waterway cleanups or Clean Air Week but as part of our daily routine) –

[6] www.businessdictionary.com/definition/transformational-change.html#ixzz2UQtnsy5X

we can keep toxins and micro-pollutants out of our air, water and food chain … and, by making these habits, we, the human species, will be able to survive for many more generations.

After a question-and-answer period, Kurt concluded the meeting. "So what did you think?" he asked Neal and Raj when they met back in his office.

"Very straightforward," said Neal, "and I was impressed by their questions. Sounded like they were ready to get onboard."

"They've seen how effective safety conversations are," Kurt responded, "and some of them have emailed me about how their safety habits have saved family members from injuries."

"Oh, by the way, Neal, I spoke with Ron Kaiser and hear he's going to travel to Texas with you for the feedback session."

"My uncle just informed me. Is he going along to babysit?"

"Babysit?" asked Raj.

"You know, keep me out of trouble," the younger man responded with a smirk, waiting for Kurt to answer.

"Not to my knowledge," Kurt replied. "Honestly though, if you can manage to convince Ron Kaiser of the value of environmental stewardship, I will name my next child after you."

"I wonder how your daughter, Shannon, would have liked being named Neal IV?" joked Raj.

"Man, you're talking big rewards, boss," laughed Neal III.

Kurt laughed as well. "But seriously, I hope you know how much what you're going to be doing in the field will impact the quality of our people's lives … and you might remind them, we're all in this together."

✦ ✦ ✦ ✦ ✦

As the company jet banked slightly to the left in preparation for landing the previous day, Neal Jacobson was able to see the patterns of progress some called "urban sprawl."

A railroad track divided the housing and schools from the thriving commercial sector, which included several older buildings from the once-small town's agricultural center.

"Man, did you see the skyscrapers as we flew over?" Kaiser said as the aircraft's wheels touched down on the runway. "Now I understand the saying, 'Everything's bigger in Texas.'"

"That it is," said Neal. "That it is."

Kaiser had been uncharacteristically quiet for the trip from the airport to the hotel. "Seeing all this open land and some of those old farmhouses makes me appreciate the finer things in life – like indoor plumbing, sewer systems and electric lights," he said finally as their cab arrived at their hotel. "Sure would hate to have to carry water and shower tonight by candlelight," he laughed.

"From what my uncle tells me, the company moved its office from downtown into this new area shortly after the airport was completed and the commuter train lines began running from here into the city center," Neal said. "Our building's supposed to be state-of-the-art with an amazing training area as well as all of the new technology available in every office. Can't wait to see it!"

"I can't wait to see the hotel bar," Kaiser responded as they checked in. "Have time for a drink … maybe two?

"Think I'll call room service later," Neal said as the two men followed the bellman to their rooms. "I'm going to go over my presentation and then call it a day."

✦ ✦ ✦ ✦ ✦

After a month's hospitalization, Janet was discharged to come home and Jessica and Kurt's lives returned to more normalcy.

"Don't help me. I can do this myself!" the older woman protested as Jess offered to push her mother's wheelchair into the house.

"Now, Mom" Jessica said patiently. "Just because they let you out of the hospital doesn't mean you're magically back to 100 percent overnight."

"But I'm not an invalid either," the older woman scowled.

"Just let us pamper you for a while," Kurt said, joining the battle, "and quit being so stubborn."

The woman looked suddenly deflated. "Okay, if you insist," she said, wryly. "But only because you're my favorite son-in-law."

Kurt and Jessica both laughed. "All that time in the hospital, she must have forgotten she only has one son-in-law," Jessica teased.

"Exactly," said Janet, winking at Kurt as Jessica pushed the wheelchair into the kitchen and positioned her mother at the kitchen table. "Hungry?"

"After all those IVs and hospital food, what do you think?" Janet said. "I could eat for days."

✦ ✦ ✦ ✦ ✦

The morning of the presentation, Ron Kaiser provided little help as Neal introduced environmental stewardship as the company's new core value – how *Safety 24/7* was being adapted to build awareness and buy-in while also employing John Kotter's *Eight Steps for Leading Change.*

"As you all know, change is often difficult," Neal acknowledged, the changes we're discussing will benefit you, your children and their children."

He was about to add some of the CEO's comments about the value of environmental stewardship for the company but was interrupted by the sirens of several emergency vehicles … and it seemed as though they had stopped nearby.

As the sirens faded, Neal completed his PowerPoint talk and then asked for any questions. As the first hands rose, the conference was interrupted by a huge explosion. This was followed by the feeling of the building being lifted off the ground and the sound of cracking timbers and shattering glass. Suddenly the lights went out and there was only blackness.

✦ ✦ ✦ ✦ ✦

Kurt's cell phone rang. He looked at the caller ID. "It's Mr. Jacobson. That's strange, him calling at this hour," he said to his wife as he answered. "Yes sir."

"There's been an explosion," the CEO began, breathlessly.

"Which site?"

Kurt could hear Jacobson struggle to take another breath. "No, no. It's not one of our sites … the explosion occurred in a building adjacent to our office – the office where Neal was holding the conference."

"Have you had word from Neal?" Kurt tried to keep the concern out of his voice. "What about Kaiser? Hear anything from Ron Kaiser? I know they made the trip together."

"All I know is there was an explosion next door that caused part of our building to collapse," Jacobson explained in an unsteady voice.

"Have you tried Neal's cell phone?" Kurt asked. "I've got Kaiser's number as well."

"Been trying Neal's phone since I got the news. No luck. We're also checking the hospitals in the area."

"Okay, let me see what I can find out and I'll get right back with you," Kurt promised.

✦ ✦ ✦ ✦ ✦

Neal found himself lying prone on the floor ... and he had lost his glasses. He reached out with his left hand and felt around in the darkness in front of him. "Must have sent them flying when I fell," he decided to himself. As he sat up and did a quick assessment, he found nothing broken. "Just a few bruises," he imagined.

Then he heard sobs, punctuated by moans and cries for help. Slowly, those who had been sitting in the conference room began to realize something disastrous had happened. Battery-powered laptops that had not been crushed cast an eerie glow through the choking dust, which had yet to settle on the debris strewn about. Though unlikely, Neal hoped no one had been killed.

"Kaiser! Ron Kaiser, can you hear me? Are you okay?"

There was moaning to his left. The younger man got down on his hands and knees and started crawling. "Ron, old man. Keep making noise. I'm trying to find you," he said as he inched along the crumbled floor.

Suddenly, he heard cursing in addition to the moaning. "Jacobson, what the hell just happened?" came a familiar voice. "Come get this #!&% piece of lumber off my leg. I think my leg is broken … no, I'm sure it's broken … maybe my ankle, too."

"Stay calm, Kaiser! I'm coming to help you!"

Feeling his way over beams, broken plaster and other rubble, Neal finally reached Ron Kaiser after what seemed like hours. At this point, the injured man was sinking in and out of consciousness. "They'll find us," he reassured Kaiser. "Just hold on."

Snapshot

Definitions

1. **Core values** – The fundamental beliefs of a person or organization, the guiding principles that dictate behavior and action. Core values help companies to determine if they are on the right path and fulfilling their business goals, and they create an unwavering and unchanging guide for behavior and decision-making in any situation.
2. **Transformational change** – A shift in the culture of an organization resulting from a change in the core values and processes that the organization has used in the past. A transformational change is designed to be organization-wide and is enacted over a period of time.

Steps Toward Stewardship

1. Be inclusive in communication, expectation and activities surrounding every new strategy, major project and/or change in the company. This creates engagement, enthusiasm and buy-in from all involved.
2. Create ongoing communication, rewards and recognition as transformational change is occurring … and once the ultimate goal is achieved, maintain these communications, rewards and recognition as employees incorporate and build on this change.
3. Dr. Kotter's *Eight-Step Process for Leading Change* can serve as a planning tool and road map for any future changes, large or small.

Additional Activities

1. Find and review case studies in which John Kotter's *Eight-Step Process for Leading Change* has been used. In a 500-word essay, describe and discuss why this process was successful.

2. Select one man-made environmental catastrophe and determine the costs to the company responsible for the damage. Comment on the other costs involved, including loss of business, community relations, etc.

3. In a 500-word paper, discuss why change is always difficult. Include some of your own ideas about how to "soften" the process of change.

4. In any change process, there are always first and last adapters, as well as "fence sitters." In a PowerPoint presentation, identify these various cohorts and how you think the process of adapting to, and embracing, change could happen more rapidly.

5. Our society has made many changes over the years – from women voting in the 1920s to the use of cell phones rather than land lines to laws requiring the use of seatbelts. Focus on any one significant change in society and describe how quickly – or not – society adapted, the motivation to adapt and whether you honestly think the change was a benefit to the majority of society.

Like It or Not, It's Personal

Kurt's day hadn't started well.

Their morning had begun with a neighbor knocking at the door. Overnight, the city's sewage plant had experienced a malfunction, allowing sewage to seep into the water supply.

"They're saying to boil any water we use," the neighbor had said. "Didn't know if you guys had turned on your TV. Our kids were watching cartoons when the announcement was made. Said it affected our entire city. Must be a pretty big deal."

After the neighbor had left, Kurt dumped his still-hot coffee into the sink and put a pot of water on the stove to boil. "Have to boil our water today," Kurt said when Jessica joined him in the kitchen. "Sewage leak at the treatment plant."

"What is it that they say, 'Timing is everything?'" grimaced Jessica. "I was going to do a few loads of clothes before I left for my meeting."

"Saved by sewage!" Kurt joked. "Hope we all have enough clean underwear to tide us over."

Jessica's smile at her husband's cleverness melted into concern. "But, no fresh water supply also means Mom won't be able to go to water therapy today. She's made such good progress, but I'm sure the hospital will close the pool until the city gives them an 'all clear' about the water quality."

She embraced her husband and kissed him goodbye. "In the meantime, have a great day."

"We'll have to defer judgment on that," said her husband as he picked up his backpack and headed toward the door. "We still haven't heard anything from Neal Jacobson after that explosion in Texas. Maybe today …," his voice trailed off as the door closed behind him.

"Nothing new," the CEO greeted Kurt, looking tired and older under the strain of the last 24 hours. "We tried to get through to the office, to our general manager in Texas, even the Red Cross all last night … and nothing. Not a word. Called Neal's cell phone. It's out of commission. Even tried the company phone Ron Kaiser always carries. Dead. My wife's beside herself. Neither of us slept."

Kurt sat down on the long, leather sofa. "Who's running our next closest job site?" he said, thinking out loud. "Maybe we can contact them to drive over to the new office and find out what's going on."

"Great idea. I'll make the call now," Jacobson said, seating himself at his desk and scrolling through the corporate phone list. "I think we have a couple of people we can count on."

"In the meantime, I'll keep trying the Texas office," Kurt offered. "Surely we can reach someone … anyone."

✦ ✦ ✦ ✦ ✦

As his uncle attempted to find his whereabouts, Neal Jacobson was absorbed by one task at hand … dragging the semi-conscious Ron Kaiser to the daylight gleaming through the opposite end of the ink-black darkness. Every piece of rubble had become an obstacle, inflicting more pain on Kaiser's already broken leg.

"Hey, take it easy," the injured man mumbled.

"I'm trying my best, Ron," the younger man said. "Would help if you weren't such a dead weight."

"You wish," Kaiser snorted.

"At least you still have a sense of humor, old man," said Neal as he stopped and rubbed the grit from his hands.

After several grueling hours, Neal stopped to rest. Trying to keep his mind off their predicament Neal said, "You know I've been thinking about the three questions I learned from the other members of the team."

"Three questions..." mumbled Kaiser struggling to stay awake and trying to ignore the pain coming from his leg."

"The three questions we need to ask ourselves about any of our actions," responded Neal.

"Oh yeah … can't think of them now. Too much pain."

"I'll help you remember," Neal offered. "To be stewards of our environment, we need to ask ourselves before we start a task:

1. **What am I doing?** It may be anything, from cleaning out a storage closet at work to restoring a job site to taking out the garbage at home.

2. **What might be environmentally risky about what I'm doing?** From placing e-waste (like used batteries) in the garbage for the landfill to using garbage bags that require hundreds of years to biodegrade.

3. **What do I do to reduce those risks?** The solution could be anything from only using paper garbage bags to checking everything that could be hazardous waste before tossing it in the garbage can at home. The same could be done at the office, also being aware on job sites for any materials that could be reduced, reused, recycled or restored.

Neal continued. "The people who came up with these three questions were talking about safety, but they also know that safe operations and environmental stewardship go hand-in-hand. Right, Kaiser?

There was no answer. Instead, Ron Kaiser had drifted into a deep sleep. Neal smiled to himself: "He's not the first person I've put to sleep."

After what had seemed like hours, the two men – tired, hungry and parched with thirst – finally reached the daylight that almost sparkled through the debris. "I'll see if I can lift one of these doors," Neal said after surveying the situation. "If I can prop one of them open, I can drag you through."

"Just don't leave me alone, buddy," came Kaiser's response.

After several tries, Neal finally had the door open and pulled the injured man through. "I'll try to find help," he promised.

Several minutes later, he returned with four uniformed men who had been working to pull survivors from the rubble that had been a four-story office building. Once Kaiser had been loaded on a stretcher, the two men were placed in an ambulance and driven to a local hospital.

Medical personnel cleaned and sutured the deeper cuts on Neal's face and arms while the older man's broken leg was immobilized. Once Kaiser had drifted into a deep sleep from the medications he had been given, Neal asked to use the hospital's phone to call his uncle.

"Thank goodness, you're safe," Fred Jacobson almost shouted when his secretary forwarded Neal's call. "And Kaiser?"

"He's resting … finally. But he raised quite a ruckus when they wanted to operate to set his broken leg," Neal said. "I think he damaged more than a few egos around here, but he's adamant about coming back home for any surgery."

"No problem. We'll send the company jet," Jacobson said. "So, how are you?"

"Just a few cuts and bruises, but I'd say I was one of the lucky ones."

"I'm just so happy to hear your voice," Neal's uncle said, "but we'll talk again as soon as we've made arrangements to get you two back here. Try and get some sleep yourself."

Over the next weeks, the details of the fire and explosion began to emerge. As one enterprising journalist found, not only was the old fertilizer plant storing 54,000 pounds of anhydrous ammonia – a substance that is flammable only at high temperatures – but it also had stockpiled more than 270 tons of ammonium nitrate, which could cause an explosion.

Further, the people in the community had grown up with the 50-year-old factory in the center of the little suburb and hadn't considered the dangers.

"It's the 'old-school' mindset," Kurt commented to his wife over dinner one night. Just because it hadn't exploded in 50 years, it probably never will."

"Or, it's our human nature. If something's there long enough – like your father's tractor seat on our patio – you soon aren't even aware it's sitting there," Jessica responded.

"I know you've never liked that thing," Kurt teased.

"No, I've grown accustomed to it. It's part of the patio."

Kurt reached across the table and squeezed her hand. "And I suppose that makes me part of the furniture?"

"Absolutely," answered Jessica as she rose to clear the table. "But you, my old friend, are the most comfortable," she added, squeezing his shoulder as she passed behind him on her way to the kitchen.

✦ ✦ ✦ ✦ ✦

Fred Jacobson ran his hand through his hair as he read a report. "Says here that old plant hadn't been inspected since 1985. Totally amazing, isn't it?"

Kurt had to agree. "That's about as unbelievable as there being no laws about where these plants can be located. If there had been, our building couldn't have been built where it was … right next to the old plant."

"Nobody offered to share any safety plans with our real estate department when we bought the building," Jacobson said. "Otherwise, somebody would have lost a sale."

Kurt picked up his copy of the incident report and studied it. "Obviously, our government doesn't have enough safety inspectors, either."[1]

"It's understandable," Jacobson conceded. "When you think about it, recent budget cuts have resulted in less government oversight … and even though environmental groups, unions and safety groups have been pushing the government to increase oversight of chemical storage and production facilities, they're no match for lobbyists wanting to minimize government fines and interference."

"Are you saying these companies, including that old fertilizer plant, should have been self-regulating?" Kurt asked.

"Better that than risk blowing a bunch of people sky high," Jacobson said, sounding impatient. "But here's the part that troubles me most. Sure, we were lucky this time. We didn't lose any employees and no one sustained a life-threatening injury," the CEO continued. "But, I just read that Texas has 44 sites that store as much or more ammonium nitrate as that plant next to our building. In all, there are 112 storage sites with the same chemicals in that state."

[1] Currently there are about 2,200 inspectors for 8 million workplaces. And OSHA typically only inspects workplaces after they receive a complaint. On top of all that, the fines involved for violations are often quite small – back in 1985, OSHA fined the West, Texas, fertilizer facility that exploded in 2013 just $30 "for a serious violation for storage of anhydrous ammonia." (The maximum fine for a serious violation is $7,000.)

Meanwhile, state health and safety regulators can't always fill in the gap. In April 2013, the Government Accountability Office issued a report noting that 22 states surveyed have failed to meet minimum workplace-safety inspection goals due to state budget cuts and reduced staffing. (www.washingtonpost.com/blogs/wonkblog/wp/2013/04/19/)

"Sounds about right. I'm thinking you'll find similar fertilizer plants in any region of the country where there's heavy agriculture," Kurt analyzed.

"Exactly," Jacobson agreed, "and I wonder how much environmental oversight there is in other countries, particularly emerging economies like India and China. But, in the meantime, I'm having ECOs with the engineering and safety departments of every location we have around the world. This near miss ..."

"Truly a miracle," Kurt said quietly. "Poor Ron Kaiser came out of the rubble with a broken leg, but his wife tells me he's doing well – as long as his therapists will put up with him."

One morning the next week, as Jim Corley pointed out during coffee with Kurt, "It's always a good idea to know what you're building next to and what, if any, risks there could be," Corley began. "The incident in Texas is a great example."

Kurt nodded. "Couldn't agree more."

"So, how's it going – your environmental stewardship orientation, I mean," asked the older man as he settled back into his chair.

"Well, first of all, I'm really pleased about how quickly our people are adopting our Environmental Conversation Opportunities," Kurt began. "It's much more popular than I ever envisioned … and the feedback I'm getting from our supervisors is very impressive. Of course, much like *Safety 24/7*, I still find myself reminding them, 'This isn't another program. It's a core value.'"

"Sounds good. Tell me more," asked Corley.

"We're already hearing about energy savings and some bottom-line cost savings, most of them coming from people remembering that whatever they do not only affects them and the company but their communities and the planet as well."

"That's exciting," Corley commented, "and how are you feeling about how it's going?"

"We're publishing our company's new worldwide rewards program for environmental stewards, and some of our offices are putting out ECO letters publicizing people who are making a difference and some of the ideas they're trying. Personally, I'm really excited about how many of our employees have bought in and are also using environmentally friendly habits at home. Let me share a few of their emails with you," he said, pulling his laptop from his backpack. "Going paperless, you know," Kurt explained as he clicked on the file and handed the computer to Corley.

"Mind if I read some of these aloud?" asked Corley.

Kurt smiled. "Be my guest."

> *"My son's high school has talked about reduce, recycle, reuse and restore. He's convinced us to try this, one step at a time, so we're trying to keep what our family generates to go into the landfill to a minimum. By doing this at home, I find myself doing the same thing at work and now my co-workers are wanting to do the same. We even had a how-to session after work one afternoon. Got some great tips!*

"These sound promising," said Corley. "Here's another:

> *"Knowing how to recognize an Environmental Conversation Opportunity and actually hold a conversation with a co-worker or family member makes me feel like I'm doing something positive for my children and their children. Taking care of the planet has become a habit for me, and I'm looking forward to learning more."*

"I'd like to read one more comment I've received. Well, it's a poem,[2] but I thought it pretty well summed up what we're hoping to accomplish," Kurt said.

> The bounties of nature are there for our use,
> But we've treated them poorly – without good excuse.
> We abused it, misused it, and threw it away,
> Now the bills coming due – and we'll all have to pay.
>
> We can choose to ignore it, and put off the debt,
> To pass it on down, to those not born yet.
> But the debt's getting bigger and bigger each year,
> And they may not be able to pay it – I fear.
>
> With each of us acting with reasonable care,
> We can use what we need – and still leave some to spare.
> We can start on the process of setting things straight,
> Clean up our environment – Before It's Too Late.
>
> Remember " Recycle," let that resource keep living,
> It's a much better life to our kids we'll be giving.
> If we keep on abusing the Earth – We should know,
> When it won't support life – 'We've got no place to go.'

"I think this says it all," Corley said after Kurt had finished reading.

[2] by Don Merrell, published with permission.

"Unfortunately, ours is not a perfect world; however, with employees moving the core value of environmental stewardship from their heads to their hearts and finally to their hands, I think your company will be a leader, not just in this country but around the world for corporations to become environmental stewards."

"As you said, this old world is not perfect," Kurt responded, "but if we all do our part, we'll definitely make a difference."

Jim Corley looked thoughtful. "When it comes right down to it, it's all a matter of survival."

SNAPSHOT

DEFINITIONS

1. **Moving the core value of environmental stewardship from head to heart to hands** – An effort to make positive changes from mentally knowing it is the right thing to do (head), moving it to a passion and commitment to making a difference (heart), to actually incorporating into your daily activities (hands).
2. **Three questions we ask before any task:**
   - ✦ What am I doing?
   - ✦ What might be environmentally risky about what I'm doing?
   - ✦ What can I do to reduce those risks?

STEPS TOWARD STEWARDSHIP

1. A culture of environmental stewardship transcends cultural differences around the world because we all want ecosystems we can depend on.

2. Focus on those wants and needs that people have in common, no matter what their country of origin.

3. A human being's underlying motivation for survival – and the survival of our planet – is universal.

4. Operations, safety and environmental stewardship are 'interdependent.'

Additional Activities

1. Choose three countries from the world map. Discuss five obvious cultural differences. Then identify at least 10 wants, needs and behaviors that they have in common.

2. Environmental stewardship must be a lifelong commitment. Discuss what you believe to be your first awareness, as a child, of the importance of caring for the environment. Then research and write a 500-word essay about the growing trend of "green funerals" and "green burials" and discuss your thoughts about a lifelong commitment to environmental stewardship.

3. Find an environmental stewardship in your community. Learn more about it and report your findings.

4. In the 20th century, there were several very loud voices advocating environmental stewardship. Identify at least three and report on their approaches to their advocacies.

5. In many situations, science and its contributions are ignored in favor of old-school mindsets. Research and find some of these mindsets prevalent today and describe the damage these mindsets have caused.

Environmental Tips: Things You Can Do

Don't Idle in the Car

How many times have you seen someone sitting in a car while it's running? Are you guilty of this? Idling wastes money and gas, and generates pollution and global warming-causing emissions. Turn your engine off if you have to wait for more than 30 seconds – except, of course, in traffic.

Drive Less

Walk, bike, carpool, or take mass transit. You'll save one pound of CO_2 for every mile you don't drive!

Use a Push Mower

We all have chores. Some of us have to mow the lawn. When you do, use your muscles instead of fossil fuels. You'll save 89 lbs. of CO_2 per year *and* you'll get some exercise.

Unplug Un-Used Electronics

Even when electronic devices, like your stereo and phone charger, are turned off, they use energy, so unplug 'em and save over 1,000 lbs. of CO_2 and $256 a year.

Put on a Sweater

Instead of turning up the heat, put on another layer. You can save 1,000 lbs. of CO_2 from entering the atmosphere and $250 a year.

Source: www.DoSomething.org

Epilogue

Kurt straightened his tie and looked into the mirror. Was the gray hair at his temples beginning to migrate into the other areas?

Jessica stood looking over Kurt's shoulder. "Mr. Bradshaw, you look charming in a tuxedo," she said, reaching around to give his tie a final adjustment.

"And you look stunning in that gown, my dear," he replied dramatically.

Jessica laughed. "Oh, you mean this old thing? Just something I found in the closet and threw on."

"Is your mother ready?"

"I'll check. The last time I saw her she was dressed and waiting for Jim Corley to pick her up for the banquet," Jessica said. "She's been as giddy as a schoolgirl since he called and asked her to go with him."

Kurt's new hybrid vehicle glided easily down the freeway and into the city. When running on battery power, there was none of the usual engine noise. "It's taken me some time to get used to not hearing all of the normal sounds," he confessed, "but it sure didn't take me long to get used to 46 miles per gallon on the highway and even higher in the city."[1]

"Better than that, my smart, handsome husband, you're helping improve the air quality for all of us," reminded Jessica. "Not to be overly dramatic, but I've worried about our future grandchildren having to wear oxygen masks when they go outdoors."

"Whoa there. Shannon's just finishing her first year of college, and I'm not ready to have anybody call me 'grandpa' just yet," Kurt joked as he stopped the car in front of the hotel and handed the keys to the parking valet. "And by the way, I'm a lucky boy," he smiled, "escorting the most beautiful woman in the world tonight."

When they reached the already noisy ballroom, Kurt seated Jessica and took his chair at the table. In a moment, Jessica waved to her mother and Jim. "I'm so glad the two of you could be here tonight."

Neal Jacobson with his wife, Patti, along with Martin Avery, Raj and their respective dates arrived shortly thereafter. "Shall we call this table the 'green team'?" Neal asked as he seated his wife.

Raj grimaced. "Makes us sound more like a lawn service, doesn't it?"

"Well, whatever name you want to choose, we can start by calling ourselves successful," said Kurt, lifting his water glass to toast everyone sitting at the table.

---

[1] www.greencarreports.com/news/1082041_best-gas-mileage-you-can-get-top-10-hybrids

"Let me second that," Jim Corley said, "because I can remember the first day we met to discuss environmental stewardship … and I must say, we've all come a long way in the last nine months."

"Nine months? No wonder there were days it felt like giving birth," Neal commented.

"Oh, like a man would know what that feels like," teased his wife.

"When you think about it, making environmental stewardship a core value is almost like having twins," Raj agreed. "You've already established a culture of safety and then you put it together with environmental awareness."

"Just like the motivation for working safely is universal, making certain we take care of the planet is, too, whether you're in the field or at …."

Kurt was interrupted by the sound of someone turning on the microphone. "Good evening all – and thank you for coming."

Fred Jacobson stood at the podium and looked around the room. "First, I want to thank you all for being here this evening, as it marks a milestone for this company, one that all of you have made possible.

"Almost a year ago, I had a vision of moving this company to the next level by making environmental stewardship a core value. I do have to admit though, I was motivated by watching one of our competitors go through an environmental disaster and all the bad things that came along with it, including financial losses and the blow to their reputation.

"I was speaking at an environmental conference last week, when someone asked me what I thought it was going to take before most people would begin conserving water. I had to think about her question for a moment before I finally answered that I honestly didn't know what it was going to take.

"One of the other panelists, a respected environmentalist, stunned the audience when she responded: 'People will begin thinking about the importance of water conservation the first time they turn on their faucet and nothing comes out.'

"Quite obviously, if that's the first inclination they have to conserve water, it's already too late," Jacobson continued. "As I said, today marks a milestone for all of us when it comes to our contributing to the health and well-being of our environment … and the planet as a whole. About 10 days ago, I quite unexpectedly received a letter I want to share with all of you. It reads:

> 'It is my pleasure to inform you that your company has been selected to receive this year's Worldwide Green Workplace Award, recognizing the company that has gone the extra mile and achieved superior results as they demonstrate and promote environmental stewardship.
>
> 'This coveted award is given to the company that has shown outstanding environmental leadership by recognizing employee contribution, promoting active involvement in serving their communities, providing excellent working conditions and contributing to a cleaner environment.
>
> 'Congratulations on this monumental achievement.
> (Signed) Sir Alfred Lawrence, Dean of Global Institute for a Sustainable Planet.'

"Martha, would you please bring out the award?" said Jacobson as the audience stood and applauded. "And Kurt Bradshaw, will you and your team please come up?"

As Kurt stood, he was joined by Raj, Neal and Martin Avery. "You're coming too, Jim," he said, waiting for the older man to join him. Together the five approached the podium.

Jacobson smiled as he began speaking. "Last year, when I shared my vision, I had no idea how we were going to achieve what I had in mind," he began. "Thanks to this team, we have not only achieved bringing environmental stewardship into our culture, we've actually made it a core value, much like we did safety several years ago.

"As we began understanding more about environmental stewardship, we also realized its integral connection to safety in our field operations. Communicating this vision – and implementing a system of rewards for team members whose innovative ideas to reduce, reuse, recycle and restore – has benefited all of us.

"I want to thank Kurt Bradshaw and his team for making my dream a reality. Kurt, please come and say a few words."

Kurt looked back at Jessica, who was beaming, and then walked to the microphone. "I'll make this brief," he began, "None of this would have been possible without your willingness to make the effort to take care of this old planet of ours."

The room was again filled with applause.

"I also want to thank each member of our team for their long hours and invaluable contributions … and I'd also like to thank Author, Harvard Professor and founder of Kotter International, Dr. John Kotter, for his *Eight-Step Process for Leading Change*, the roadmap we used to become environmental stewards, both at work and at home, 24/7.

"Many of you don't know Dr. Jim Corley, the gentleman to my left, but Jim, I can never repay you for your contributions and the hours you've spent mentoring, teaching, guiding and reassuring this team.

"Finally, I must thank my wife, Jessica, for her ongoing love and encouragement, Mr. Jacobson for his belief in me and his leadership and, finally, to my team – Raj, Martin and Neal – for being there with their energy, desire for excellence and their willingness to step out of their comfort zones almost daily in order to achieve our many and varied goals.

"Thanks to all of you for making this such a memorable day for the company. You are our true environmental champions!"

After the team had returned to their table and Jessica had given her husband a quick kiss, Jacobson had another surprise.

"Most of you know Ron Kaiser, am I right?"

Some of those seated around the ballroom booed in good fun while others applauded.

"I'll take that response as a 'yes,'" Jacobson said, "but to know Ron is to love him. (More applause.) Anyway, you all probably remember Ron's close call in Texas and his road to recovery. Since he's now off his crutches, I'd like to ask him to come up and say a few words. So as they say on television, Ron Kaiser … come on down!'"

While still in rehab, Kaiser had almost regained his full strength. He walked swiftly to the microphone.

"He's the one," Janet whispered to her daughter, who was seated beside her. "He's the gentleman who was so annoying in my water aerobics class."

"Mr. Jacobson is kind to allow me some time to tell you my story," Kaiser began.

"When we first began discussing environmental stewardship, I'll admit, I was one of the biggest blockers … called Kurt and his team a bunch of tree huggers … even worse, but there are ladies present, so I won't go into detail because I'm a gentleman."

"Oh yeah, Kaiser. Sure you are," someone in the audience heckled in a good-natured way.

"There's an old saying about the only way to get a mule's attention is to hit him between the eyes with a two-by-four," Kaiser continued. "In my case, it took a building falling on me to learn something about the environment and how it goes hand-in-hand with safety.

"It also took constant reminders from a woman in my rehab group – and who is with us tonight – to show me how, with just a little effort, my family and I can live without helping destroy our planet," he said. "Janet, please stand and take a bow."

With the encouragement of Kurt, Jessica and Corley, Janet finally stood and waved to the audience.

"Don't let appearances fool you. This little grandmother is not only a powerhouse when it comes to taking care of our environment. She also can be a real pain in the butt," said Kaiser, "but along with my experience in Texas, knowing Janet has changed my life. I even turn off the water now when I'm brushing my teeth … and we recycle every Saturday … all thanks to Janet."

Kaiser continued. "I would also like to take this opportunity to publicly thank Neal Jacobson for literally saving my life. He also helped teach me the importance of making our company environmentally aware. Well ... what else could we talk about while we waited for help?

"And, I want to thank all of you for your prayers and support during my hospitalization ... and thank you, too, for making this thing called 'environmental stewardship' more than something you talk about. I mean, you people not only talk the talk, but you walk the walk. I see it every day, and I'm proud to be part of a company that not only takes care of its people but also our planet. Thank you from the bottom of my heart."

Jacobson hugged Kaiser and took the microphone. "Thank you, Ron. Glad to have you back in one piece!"

The CEO's smile melted into a somber expression. "I'd like to make one more brief but important announcement. As all of you remember, heaven gained another little angel with the sudden passing of my assistant Martha Samuel's little daughter, Sophie, after a courageous battle with asthma.

"Following that unexpected tragedy, we created the SOPHIE Says fund (www.sophiesays.org) in an effort to prevent other unnecessary deaths due to environmental pollution. Today, in less than a year, thanks to contributions from all of you and many others who want to protect our next generations with a healthier environment, SOPHIE's fund now totals over $10,000.[2]

The audience stood and applauded as Martha, Sophie's mother, came to the microphone.

"The response to SOPHIE Says has been totally overwhelming to me and my family," she said. "We've come a long way, but we still need

[2] A portion of the price of each *Environment 24/7* book will be contributed to SOPHIE Says, and additional contributions to this or other worthwhile funds would be appreciated.

your help … and that includes getting out the word and remembering Sophie any time you're tempted to take short cuts that will negatively impact our clean air, clean water and our environment in general. So, thank you for honoring my daughter. We miss her terribly, but Sophie was a little girl with big dreams so, through this fund, Sophie continues to live in our hearts."

The audience stood and applauded, many with tears in their eyes.

"I don't know when I've enjoyed an evening out more," said Jessica as she and Kurt were leaving the ballroom, "and I thought it especially nice for the hotel to make that generous donation to SOPHIE Says."

Just as Kurt was opening the door, Jacobson stopped him. "Do you have another minute?" he asked Kurt.

"Absolutely. And, what a wonderful evening of nice surprises," responded Kurt.

Jacobson shook his head. "It's been a long evening, so I won't keep you, but I would like to meet with you tomorrow morning to discuss my next vision for this company."

Kurt nodded affirmatively. "Sure, Mr. Jacobson, but can you share anything more with me?"

"You have done such an outstanding job leading both our Safety and Environmental culture changes," Jacobson paused. "It's time we focused on Health 24/7."

About the Authors

Gregory M. Anderson spent the past decade as president of one of the largest consulting and training companies specialized in providing behavior-based safety and leadership training for companies operating in high-risk environments around the world.

Greg is considered to be a leading authority on helping companies change their safety culture and, in 2006, co-authored *Safety 24/7* with Robert L. Lorber. To date, the book has sold over a quarter of a million copies and is available in eight languages.

A graduate of the University of Southern California, Greg is a true internationalist having lived, worked and traveled in 50 countries as he battled oil fires in Kuwait, provided infrastructure for military personnel in Haiti and drilled for oil in North Africa. He currently provides independent consulting services while living in Texas with his wife and three daughters.

Dr. Richard Haut is currently the director of Energy Production at the Houston Advanced Research Center (HARC) in The Woodlands, Texas. Dr. Haut also serves as the program director for the Environmentally Friendly Drilling (EFD) program in partnership with Texas A&M University, other universities, industry and environmental organizations. The objective of EFD is to provide unbiased science to address environmental issues associated with petroleum drilling and production. EFD was recognized by the Interstate Oil and Gas Compact Commission, receiving their Chairman's Environmental Partnership award in 2009.

Dr. Haut's technical background includes a Master's degree and a Ph.D. in Engineering. Just as important as the formal education is what he learned from his parents: *Leave the world better than you found it; Take only what you need; Make amends if you harm someone or something.* He has been featured in the *Wall Street Journal* on multiple occasions, and also in *Echoes*, the alumni magazine of the Rose-Hulman Institute of Technology. Dr. Haut is a frequent source for the media with regard to environmental issues. In addition, he has given Congressional testimonies on multiple occasions and assisted the National BP Deepwater Horizon Gulf Spill and Offshore Drilling Commission.

Tom Williams serves as a Senior Advisor to the Environmentally Friendly Drilling program, an organization he co-founded in 2005 while working as a Vice President at Noble Corporation. He has been in the energy business for over 30 years as an operator and later in his career in the management and commercialization of new energy technologies. He held senior executive positions at the U.S. Department of Energy and Department of Interior during the Bush Administration from 1989 to 1993. Tom has continued to be involved in a variety of organizations and activities, developing and applying technologies for the oil and gas industry and research though fostering cooperation between the government and private sector. He is well known in the industry and has authored numerous energy publications, presentations and articles and has served on a number of energy organizations, associations, public and privately held corporations.

Acknowledgments

by Greg Anderson

I believe you can learn something from every person you meet, and I want to take this opportunity to thank those people who have shared their knowledge with me:

Richard Haut and Tom Williams for having the insight to recognize how the *Safety 24/7* principles could go from saving people's lives to saving ecosystems. You are truly making a difference on this planet we call home.

Alice Adams for believing anything we do together is possible. You are one phenomenal lady.

Bob Lorber, for your input on *Safety 24/7.*

My daughters, Brittany, Makenzie and Kendall, for all they are teaching me about how to be a father.

My wife, Robin. This book would be twice as long if I wrote down all the things I am grateful for; I wish everyone could be as lucky as I am.

Finally, for those who walked beside me on my journey, you know who you are.

Acknowledgments

by Richard Haut

There are numerous folks who have crossed my path, each one having provided insight into the world around me, enhanced the experience and given me – sometimes without their knowledge – direction.

Greg Anderson and Tom Williams for their dedication and drive in making this book a reality.

To the third musketeer, Dave Burnett, who keeps the other two of us real.

My greening mentors. In particular, Pliny Fisk and Brian Yeoman, who constantly remind me that I can do good things.

The men at Lord of Life Lutheran Church in The Woodlands for keeping it all grounded.

Kirk Petersen, my lifelong friend, who assisted in placing the skeletons in the closet and works side-by-side with me to keep them there.

Annette, my partner and companion for life. Thank you for helping me throughout this life, more than you ever will know.

Our children, Naomi, Noah and Ruthanne, their spouses, Sage, Beth and Hunter, all their children and foster children, past, present and future, for teaching me about the circle of life.

My parents, Dick and Ruth Haut, gone from this life, and never to be forgotten. They started it all.

Finally, my sister, Sue Hart, who is always there for me to antagonize.

Acknowledgments

by Tom Williams

My former CEO at Noble Corporation, Jim Day demonstrated that a company can develop a stellar safety culture to lead an industry, inspire a new generation of leaders and be profitable. His vision of developing a similar environmental culture in the energy business challenged me to apply what I had learned in my career to form the Environmentally Friendly Drilling (EFD) program. This crazy idea would not have been possible without my talented and "like-minded" partners and friends, David Burnett and Rich Haut.

I inherited my passion for fishing from my dad, Clyde Williams, who showed me it was secondary to the love of our country, family and the environment.

My best friend, Jim Toombs, who shares a belief that having any success in life comes from having good friends, luck, skill, and lots of persistence.

The nicest person in the world is my wife, Gale, who has tolerated, supported and encouraged my passion for the EFD program despite the lifestyle compromises. We would do it all again in a heartbeat.

Greg Anderson's talk about *Safety 24 /7* made Rich and I know that a book on an environmental culture would be an important tool for getting everyone on the same page, from the student debating career choices to the guy on the rig floor to the CEO. We greatly appreciate his excellent work and passion. This is a story on how a right culture is truly developed.

Order Form

1-30 copies $17.95 31-100 copies $16.95 100+ copies $15.95

Environment 24/7 ____ copies X ________ = $_____

Shipping & Handling Charges $_____

Sales Tax 8.25% (Texas only) $_____

Total* (U.S. Dollars Only) $_____

**Excludes Sales Tax – Except in Texas*

Domestic U.S. (AK, HI add'l) Shipping & Handling Charges
(Single point delivery. 'Handling Charge' fee only, w/use of company shipping account.)
International Quoted on Individual Order Basis - See Contact Details Below

Total $ Amount	Up to $50	$51-$99	$100-$249	$250-$1199	$1200-$2999	$3000+
Charge	$9	$16	$25	$40	$85	$130

Name ______________________________ Job Title ______________

Organization ______________________________ Phone ______________

Email ______________________________ Fax ______________

Shipping Address ______________________________

City ______________________________ State __________ ZIP __________

Billing Address & Contact ______________________________
(if different than shipping)

Purchase Order Number (if applicable) ______________________________

Charge Your Order: ❑ MasterCard ❑ Visa ❑ American Express

Credit Card Number ______________________________ Exp. Date ______________

Signature ______________________________

FAX Orders to: 281.466.2617

Phone: 281.651.5648

Website: www.environment247.org

Mail orders to:

RGA Holdings, LLC
P.O. Box 131120
Spring, TX 77393
USA

Environmental Tips: Things You Can Do

Buy Organic Food

The chemicals used in modern agriculture aren't just bad for your body, they also pollute the water supply and are mostly made of petroleum.

Bring Cloth Bags to the Market

When the check-out person asks, "Paper or plastic?," say, "Neither." Using your own cloth bag reduces waste and requires no additional energy.

Turn Off Your Computer

Shut if off when you're not using it and save 200 lbs. of CO_2. Conserve energy by using your computer's "sleep mode" instead of a screensaver.

Eat Your Greens

The average American diet is full of meat products and thus contributes an extra 1.5 tons (that's 2,500+ lbs.) of greenhouse gases per year, compared with a vegetarian diet. Eating 20 percent less meat makes the same impact as switching to a hybrid car!

Spread the Word

Get out there and tell your friends and loved ones about the small steps they can take to help Mother Earth. A little goes a long way!

Source: www.DoSomething.org